CHARLES THE HAMMER

The enemy approached with a sound of distant thunder. "Stand close, men of Frankland . . . stand close!" The combined armies of Frankland and Aquitaine, with Charles Martel as their leader, lay waiting to halt the threatened Mohammedan invasion of Tours in what is now France.

The story of the man who led these forces to victory in the historic battle of 732 A.D. is told in *Charles the Hammer*. In this suspenseful tale of the Dark Ages, Shane Miller traces the career of Charles as he struggles to bring peace and order to his own and surrounding nations. In his efforts to unite Frankland, we see him battle against the jealousies of his family and the leaders of the other French nations. We also see him work closely with Boniface, the missionary, to spread and preserve the Christian civilization of the Western World.

Named the Hammer after the successful Battle of Tours, Charles was the tool that shaped all history by his powerful drive to broaden the influence of Frankland over Europe and bring into being the country which we now know as France.

"A biography full of adventure and action."
Los Angeles County Board of Education

AUTHOR'S NOTE

Rome and Greece recorded their history almost day by day, and it is no trouble at all to reconstruct the pictures of the forums and marketplaces of their great cities. We are as familiar, too, with their great men and women as we are with those of our own times. We can know through their arts what they thought and said, how they dressed, and what they looked like. As the Roman Empire crumbled away, however, the deep shadows of the Dark Ages engulfed the arts, the crafts, and the written word. The lights of Europe were extinguished, for those who came as invaders could not read or write. For a long time few records were kept.

A story from this period such as the life and times of Charles Martel—and even up to the time of Charlemagne—has to be put together from fragments. As an archaeologist puts together a Grecian vase from the broken shards which he has dug out of the earth and assembled, so it was in putting together the incidents that make up this story. The main facts are few; details are even more scarce and what few contemporary chronicles there are give the figures of those times the legendary quality of sheer mythology.

Yet in painstakingly fitting the fragments together with their dates and places, a surprisingly consistent pattern emerges that throws the figure of Charles Martel into relief. By implication, Charles, leader of the Franks, and St. Boniface, "Apostle of Germany," were men who dealt realistically with the situation of their times. The fruits of their efforts are with us today and tell their own story.

Charles the Hammer

The Story of
CHARLES MARTEL

Written and Illustrated by
SHANE MILLER

This book was originally published as
The Hammer of Gaul.

A TURRET BOOK / Guild Press, New York

Published with ecclesiastical approbation.

PUBLISHED BY GUILD PRESS, INC.

CONTENTS

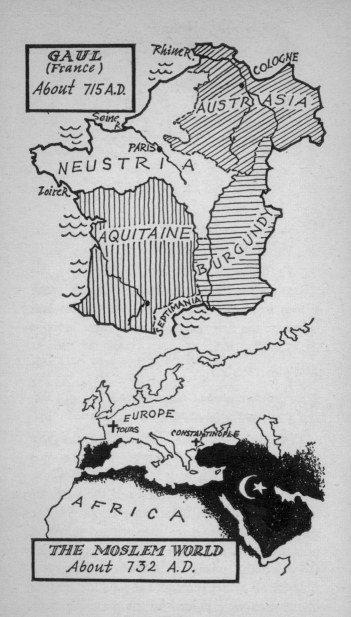

GAUL
(France)
About 715 A.D.

Rhine R.

COLOGNE

AUSTRASIA

Seine R.

PARIS

NEUSTRIA

Loire R.

AQUITAINE

BURGUNDY

SEPTIMANIA

EUROPE

✝ TOURS

CONSTANTINOPLE ✝

AFRICA

THE MOSLEM WORLD
About 732 A.D.

CHAPTER ONE

The Monk and the Soldier

Sharp blew the winds which bore the battle sounds from the north, sharp as the pikes and lances of the Frisians and Saxons who brought the war. Blustering, too, they were, and rude as their threats to the peace of Austrasia. For this was the year 714, in the city of Cologne on the River Rhine, and the Frankish warriors were everywhere springing to arms.

At the door of the tower prison within the gates of this same city, a travel-stained monk was knocking, his robe whipped by these same winds.

To the man-at-arms who opened the port, the monk held up a ring. Whatever its magic was, the gate swung open and the man stepped inside. A brief consultation followed, then the guard led the way to the cubicle where sat the scribe responsible for all prison records. The aquiline features of the man were lighted by the guttering lamp

7

overhead; his scrutiny was long and keen but respectful as the monk answered his questions.

"I am Osric, of the community of Exeter in Wessex. I am returning to Britain from Rome, where I have spent the past five years. When I arrived here in Cologne a few days ago I learned that a noble prisoner was being held here. Perhaps I might be allowed to visit him to offer what consolation I can."

A ghost of a smile flickered across the face of the scribe and the guard turned his head away suddenly. Seemingly these were mummers acting out a well-rehearsed play; all questions had actually been answered by the flashing of the ring.

The scribe addressed the guard:

"See if the—ahem—prisoner will see the visitor."

The guard scurried off down the passage and the scribe returned to his tasks.

Within the space of fifteen minutes the visitor was ushered into a cell, larger than most, but almost totally lacking in light. Some embers glowed in a brazier and a patch of light from the corridor outside illuminated one wall. The monk stood for a moment to accustom his eyes to the gloom, while a turnkey made fast the cell door from the outside. The guard and the turnkey went off together.

A husky voice sounded out of the darkness: "The turnkey told me that I could expect a visitor today but he did not choose to tell me his name."

The cleric identified himself quickly and concluded with the words, "Sir, I am here to fulfill the office of my Order. How long has it been since you have spoken with your confessor?"

The silence that followed was broken presently by the sound of the prisoner's movements as he shifted his position on the rude pallet.

"I have been here for almost a year," he said. "No one has concerned himself about my misdeeds—or my triumphs, either, for that matter."

The monk spoke and even in the dark the prisoner knew he was smiling. "What can be the sins of a man so well sheltered from the ways of the world and its temptations? In truth, I might have spent the time in a better way. Yet before I leave, would you care to speak with a friend?"

The silence was longer this time. The gentle sarcasm of the monk worked slowly through the prisoner's mind.

"Good brother, I am a soldier. My thoughts are few and simple. First, how am I to get out of here? The second, which follows most naturally, has to do with the old she-dragon who put me here. The third has to do with returning to my profession. I understand that they can use a few soldiers in these stirring times!"

"I am sure they can." The monk's tone was dry. He reached over, grasped the prisoner's arm in the dark and drew him to his feet. Slowly the monk moved him into the lighted area of the wall and stood gazing thoughtfully at the face of the young man so revealed. The eyes were intelligent, the hair and beard were unkempt, the sheepskin cloak was grimy over his tunic; but all this could be easily remedied. What mattered was that the prisoner had kept his health and strength.

"You have not fared too badly, Charles. They have fed you fairly well, I see, and there is a brazier with glowing coals. Many another prisoner has suffered more. Your clothing is still whole, your coverings warm and—"

"Yes, yes,"—the young man's voice was irritable —"but anyone knows what happens to a sword which remains in its sheath. I am twenty-six years old. Even now the enemies of my people are at the door. What am I doing here?"

The good brother waited.

"A moment ago you called me by name. Then you must also know that I am Charles, son of Pepin II, mayor of the palace of Austrasia. I am not even a noble. And yet Plectrude, my stepmother, has confined me here—for what? For merely being underfoot. For merely being alive!"

"It is not quite like that, Charles," remonstrated the monk gently. "When your father died, he made Plectrude regent over Neustria and Austrasia until her children were old enough to rule. But you must remember, before everything else, Plectrude is a mother. Any woman will fight for her children and sacrifice herself, if necessary, for their security. You were a soldier; at what moment would you take it into your head to seize the throne for yourself? These were *her* thoughts, Charles. Not mine."

"Then she *did* send you!" The young man's voice shook in his fury. "She must have sent you, for you know her very thoughts. Does she then fear me? Even here? So now she sends you to plead with me, to present her cause!"

The monk held up his hand. "Nonsense, Charles. I was sent, of course, but not by Plectrude. No."

Charles fought to control himself. "There is too much about all this that I don't understand. Why have you come here? Who sent you?"

Before answering his questions, the monk allowed time for the young man's anger to cool. Then out of the darkness came the sound of laughter to Charles' ears, the laughter of a man who had experienced life deeply and found it good. The bright note infected Charles, and his anger fled away; his teeth flashed white in his soiled face. Then his smile faded when he heard the monk's next words.

"I am here, Charles, to seek the man who will bring unity and strength and purpose to the people of Gaul, as your father tried to do. I am seeking the soldier who can bring order out of chaos and who will govern the Frankish peoples wisely and well. Until a moment ago, I thought I had found him."

"And now?"

Suddenly it dawned on Charles that he stood in the presence of no ordinary cleric. He became alert. He sensed that he was poised at a moment of his life from which everything would later be reckoned. Everything to come could conceivably have its beginning here in this gloomy prison cell. This—somehow—was the most important moment of his life.

"I was looking for a man of stature, Charles, a man of sinew and character who could bring together all the Frankish peoples to form a great nation. I was looking for a man who, by the grace of the Holy Spirit, would know what was wanted in this hour of his country's history, who would know how to go about supplying the needs and binding up the wounds of men and bringing peace to Gaul. Not just for the sake of the Frankish peoples—no, but to give the rest of the world a shining example and a code of laws to live by here and now.

"Instead what do I find?" The monk's voice was gentle but very firm. "A man who calls himself a soldier but who lives for the moment of release from his prison so that he can strike back at a woman and her children! What a satisfying thing that must be!"

Charles reached out suddenly and grasped the monk with fingers of steel. At the same time Osric caught hold of Charles with an equally firm grip. The two men faced each other. If the monk could make no move, no more could Charles. In truth, the two were perfectly matched in physical strength but, seemingly, there were other forces at work. Charles suddenly released his hold and leaned against the wall. He passed a hand over his eyes, a hand that trembled from rage that was suddenly spent.

"What would you have me do?"

"Forgive her, Charles, forgive her."

Again the prisoner's temper flared. "You don't understand, do you?" he cried. "Not even now." His voice rose bitterly. "What of Rotruda, my wife? What of my two sons, Carloman and Pepin? I tell you that the old she-dragon has them all so completely under her thumb that none of them dares to visit me here for fear of her anger. You want me to forgive her in the face of all that?"

"The man I have in mind will be a great man, Charles," the monk said and his voice softened. "He will be a great man because he is strong enough to be gentle. His power will be the power of love and there is no armor in the world against that."

Osric watched the effect of his words as they registered on the face of the prisoner. Because he was a Saxon, whose people had made their way into Britain by the power of the sword, he understood perfectly the difficulty that the Frankish mind would encounter with the idea of love—as Osric meant it in the Christian sense. The whole world throughout ages to come would struggle with the meaning of that word.

Charles suddenly leaned against the wall.

For the second time, Charles put the question, "What would you have me do?"

Hardly had the monk begun to give his answer when the turnkey returned to end the visit. The cell-door bolt shot back and his cracked voice rose querulously, telling the visitor his time was up.

"I must go now, I see, Charles. But I will be back. Have no fear. We have much to discuss—much," Osric said.

Many were the thoughts and ideas that flowed through Charles' mind after the monk had gone. As a soldier, his life had been spent in terms of deeds and actions. The world of ideas was an unknown land. The Franks had been a roving people, as were their Germanic brothers across the Rhine. Most important to them were tools and weapons, food and drink, or the struggle to obtain and hold these life-giving items. The Frank's oath of fealty was to his chief or king, not to his country, since, in days gone by, one never knew where his "country" would be for the night! Charles had been taught that the heroic warrior was the man who struck first, yet the ideas of Christianity were new and interesting with their expressions of love and forgiveness. Who knew for certain? Perhaps the Christian God, as described by the missionaries, might be a more powerful ally in war than the forest deities. Perhaps He could better bring forth the fruits of the earth and more abundant crops. Many Germans, as the Franks had been originally, had accepted conversion and baptism for all sorts of reasons. Maybe the monk was right when he cautioned Charles to forgiveness.

Osric well knew the task before him. As a barbaric Saxon who had embraced the new religion, he was well aware of the odds against him as he sought to bring light to the mind of the imprisoned Frankish soldier. He had been to Rome and had seen the wonders of the civilization that had formerly ruled the whole known world by law and order. It was disturbing to observe how little anybody cared or even knew that here in Gaul there had once been good roads, cleared fields, well-ordered markets, and the pleasures of literature and the drama! The Franks had entered a land already being devoured by the encroaching forests. They did not even have the curiosity to wonder at the traces of the great civilization which had sunk beneath this sea of vegetation. To a Frank, in those days, the forest was the rightful home of a man, and the rule of tooth and claw was the only law there was.

When the door of the dungeon closed behind him again, Osric found that somehow since his visit yesterday a change had come about. Charles was awaiting him not in bored indifference or resentment but with eager interest.

"Brother Osric, you have given me much to think about since yesterday. What have you to tell me today?"

"Charles, do you know who built the city of Cologne?" the monk asked.

"No. Does it matter?"

The cleric sighed. He began by telling of the Roman legions which had been stationed here for many generations. When he pointed out that the valor and reputation of these troops were such that no enemy dared attack them at Cologne, Charles was interested. Soldiering was something he had known through experience. He marveled that the Roman troops had lived here for so long without having to fight a single battle, particularly since he understood that the Saxons had been one of the tribes held down to their own side of the Rhine.

"Exactly!" Osric was making his point and was quietly jubilant. "Today as we sit here these same Saxons, with the Frisians and Neustrians, are driving hard from the north and may win their way to Cologne to pillage, burn, and plunder at almost any moment. Austrasia has done little to stop them. This is the present situation, whether we like it or not. The legions left here three hundred years ago, Charles. They will not be back. What will take their place?"

The monk continued. He related his knowledge of the past as if it were a bard's tale and Charles listened with his eyes glowing. Osric knew that Charles would better understand what he was saying if he told the story of the past in the Frankish manner. Often on a winter night,

Charles had sat before a crackling fire listening to the wandering minstrel tell in song of the heroic deeds of his forefathers. It was the way an unlettered people heard its own past glories, retold again and again to spur on current generations to like heroism. Osric also knew that Charles would remember what he heard, for, whereas an educated man stores much of his knowledge in books and written notes, the unlettered man must retain what he has heard through memory alone.

Once again the glories of old Rome were relived through the monk's telling, the story of how Roman law had kept peace and order throughout the known world for so long. He spoke of tilled fields, well-kept orchards, good roads, and feats of building and construction which even yet thrust up their skeletons throughout Gaul. These were remains of what had been baths, aqueducts, fortresses, temples, and theaters, beautiful beyond describing. All this had been maintained by a few well-disciplined legions, strategically placed.

Yet, when the dikes broke, through internal weakness, the barbarian hordes swept down into Rome like a great sea. There was no force or army left to cope with the situation. The strong took what they wanted over the bodies of the helpless; there was no compassion, no pity. People behaved like sheep without a shepherd, while the wolves among men devoured them at will. The "Pax Romana," two hundred years of peace maintained by less than half a million armed legionnaires scattered throughout the known world, was only a dim memory. For many, the end of the world had come.

Why was it that, left to his own devices, man always seemed to descend to the rule of tooth and claw? The Romans had controlled the naturally lawless through the threat of arms. Yet the problem itself had never been solved. How would one go about teaching men to stop acting like animals?

The warrior spoke out: "Why, as for that, good brother, I would let my good sword speak. That is a language that anybody understands."

The monk thoroughly enjoyed the humor of this. "I'm sure you would, Charles. Yet not even Rome could make men *want* to stop fighting. That is the problem. Not the fighting itself. No, Charles, the remedy lies in something that has never been tried before—to man's knowledge. I speak of a rule of law to come from the heart, the law of brotherhood and compassion, to take the place of force of arms.

"This is the task that the Church has taken upon itself, Charles. Will you help?"

It seemed to Charles that the hour allowed for the monk's visit had passed entirely too quickly when the turnkey's voice was heard in the corridor. Long after the visitor's departure, Charles' head spun with the host of new impressions and ideas which his mentor had implanted within it. In truth, the world was larger than it seemed!

The prisoner found himself filled with a strange excitement at the core of which seemed to rest a grain of hope. There was something in the air, something which would involve him.

The next day, the brother made his way again through the narrow winding streets to Charles' prison. New levies of troops were being marched in as local landgraves or governors supplied their quotas of fighting men. One street was so choked with men and horses that Osric was a full fifteen minutes in forcing his way across. The accompanying din was one vast sea of sound.

As Osric entered the dungeon again, Charles was already pacing up and down. Much of the time was spent in answering Charles' questions. The atmosphere was charged with his excitement.

"How will it begin?" was his most often repeated question. He had been raised as a nominal Christian. All of his forbears back to Clovis' time had been Christians. He himself had been baptized by St. Rigobert, bishop of Rheims. Yet it had seemed to him that much concern had been shown in a life to come, a future existence not even remotely connected with life today in Gaul, here and now. And how could a soldier serve in a kingdom where, by the very nature of things, there would be no need for soldiers?

"Hear me, Charles." The voice of Osric was gentle but forceful in its persistence. "There will always be a need for strong men to protect the helpless while peace and order are being restored.

There will always be need for soldierly attributes of courage, forthrightness, and right planning, tempered with justice and mercy. What kind of soldier will you be, Charles? An able administrator protecting the helpless, or a mere conqueror and plunderer?"

The brother did not wait for an answer but reached into the brazier and drew out a dead coal. Quickly he moved to the square of light on the wall and sketched a crude map of the land which would one day be known as France. Neustria was shown to be in roughly the same area as modern Normandy. East of Neustria was Austrasia with its capital at Metz. The city of Cologne was indicated by a circle north of Metz. Austrasia occupied roughly the area now known as Lorraine and West Germany. Charles could see now, as perhaps never before, that Austrasia held the key to the situation. To the east lay the war-like Germans; to the north lay the land of the Frisians and Saxons, who were now pressing hard on Austrasia's northwest territories. Neustria, herself too weak to throw off the rule of Austrasia, as administered by Plectrude, had allied herself with the Frisian and Saxon hordes, thus constituting a threat to Austrasia from the west.

Little wonder Frankish trumpets were sounding the alarm!

Until the turnkey appeared again to bring an end to the visiting hour, the soldier and the monk discussed the situation as shown by the map. Then

Quickly he sketched a crude map.

Brother Osric bade the prisoner farewell, and this time Charles knelt for the monk's blessing.

"Will you come again?" Charles' voice was a shade wistful. Something told him that he would never see this man again.

"This is my third and last visit, Charles. Shortly you will understand why. These are exciting times and events will move swiftly. But, Charles, in spite of all that may happen, try to remember some of the things I have told you. These are important things and a great many people will be affected by them."

And with that he was gone.

Alone in his cell once more, Charles went back to the map. He studied the terrain as shown and his soldier's eye caught the weak link in the enemy's situation. If an Austrasian army were to move rapidly northward and then drive westward before the Neustrians could join forces with the Frisians and Saxons, pressure from the west could be relieved. Neustria would then collapse, being herself too weak to carry out her rebellion. Next, by wheeling eastward, he was sure, the Frisian and Saxon flank could be turned. Austrasian reserves could come up and reduce the remnants. It would be well worth trying.

His restlessness was almost more than he could bear and it was not until very late that night that he succeeded in dropping off to sleep. He was awakened only a few minutes later—or so it seemed—by loud Frankish voices in the corridor.

"Stand aside, scum, or by the bones of my grandfather I will crack thy crown," a familiar voice rang out. "This way, this way."

The hastily awakened turnkey was protesting in his high voice. Behind all this was the sound of Frankish laughter, huge gusts of it, with more Frankish than Gallo-Roman speech.

"By the gods of my fathers," the voices sounded nearer, "where are you, Charles?"

The door was being unfastened and Charles helped to swing it open. A round dozen of burly warriors stamped in and Charles was overwhelmed by the embraces and jovial slaps of all his old comrades-in-arms. These were his "leudes" —his people—and his joy at seeing them again warmed his whole soul.

"Well then, my brother," the voice of Childebrand sounded in the darkness, "what are you waiting for? Come! Come! How does it feel to be a free man again, eh? A torch here, somebody, so that we can see what we are doing."

Austrasian nobles, fully aroused to the danger threatening their homeland, had taken action. Whatever Plectrude's talents were as an administrator in times of peace, these were times which required the hand of a strong man. Charles, son of Pepin II, was their choice, a strong son, they hoped, of a strong father.

Within a matter of minutes, Charles was standing outside the prison where he had spent nearly a year, breathing the cool night air in freedom!

CHAPTER TWO

The Duke of Austrasia

A file of armed men moved through the narrow alleys of the city of Cologne; the light of several torches was enough to show the way. They encountered only a few sentinels in the dark as they proceeded to the small court where Childebrand had left the horses under the watchful eyes of seven or eight men-at-arms. Charles, for his part, was feeling almost giddy in his sudden freedom. Something within him made him want to shout, to sing and dance for the sheer joy of his release.

"And now, lads"—the shadowy figure of Childebrand spoke—"we have been delayed long enough. To Metz with all speed!"

The company left the city, moving southwest and then south. This was the old Roman road which had brought the legions to "Colonia Agrippina," as Cologne had been known in those days.

This was the road, too, by which the traders and merchants had made their way to the Rhine, to cross and trade with the German tribes. To the troop of Franks, however, who were now moving swiftly along it, there had always been a road here and always would be. This rich heritage they accepted, like children, without question.

Meanwhile, Childebrand, his cloak billowing out behind him like the wings of a bat, related to Charles the events at the "Palatium," the name of Pepin's former palace in Metz. These events had been what had led to their ride to Charles' prison.

Plectrude, surrounded by her councilors and advisors, had left Cologne and returned to Metz for the time being. However, they had failed to move in any direction with any kind of plan. This had led to various factions in the court springing up and adding more and more confusion to the situation. One party quarreled with another until at last no one could agree on anything. All of this, of course, had only confirmed the Neustrians in their quest for independence—and their allies, the Saxons and Frisians, in their lust for plunder.

At last a group of men arose, landholders and their vassals, who felt the time had come to take action. A strong man must be found to take a stand and put an end to these difficulties once and for all. Skillfully, Childebrand had put his brother's name before the group. There was some discussion, but all at last agreed that Charles, son of Pepin, was the right man.

"And do you agree with this, my brother?" Charles' gay laughter rang out. The cool fresh air, the exercise, the sense of freedom, of escape from a dark dungeon, all combined to make him almost reel in the saddle.

"Why, as for that, with you to give the orders and me to make the songs, Neustria should look to her defenses!"

"And the Frisians and Saxons?" Charles asked. "What of them? Will they also take to their heels at my first shout or your sour notes? Perhaps we should have a different music for them?"

Childebrand laughed, drew his sword, and struck a ringing blow on the shield of the man riding next to him. "Let that be the note for the Frisians and Saxons," he said.

Both men were sons of Pepin, mayor of the palace of Frankland; both had been born of Alpaïde, and a strong bond had always existed between them. Whereas Charles was the warrior, Childebrand was the poet. They had never been rivals, for each had pursued his own destiny without being challenged by the other.

Charles' playful moment passed quickly and his questions followed; first, where were the invaders and the Neustrian forces? What had Plectrude done to halt them? Who was the duke in charge of mobilizing the forces of Austrasia? Had any actual fighting taken place, and if so, where? Only at the last did he ask about Osric, the monk who had visited him in prison.

"As for Osric," laughed Childebrand, as if he were about to tell the story he enjoyed most, "this good man arrived one day at the palace and questioned this one and that one. He said he had come from Rome and was looking for a strong man to save Gaul. He even talked to Plectrude, poor man, although strangely enough she listened to him when she would listen to no one else. He said some amazing things, and in the end she handed him her ring which would gain him admittance to your cell."

"Plectrude's ring?" Charles could not believe his ears.

"He was carrying the ring when he came from Plectrude's chambers; he showed it to us and we —that is, the barons and I—explained the whole situation to him. The next thing we knew, he was gone. Later he sent word for us to join him in Cologne, which we did. The rest you know."

This was difficult for Charles to believe. The one woman he had always considered to be his greatest enemy had been instrumental in releasing him from prison.

"Perhaps this will help," said Childebrand, and he passed Charles the familiar ring. "Osric gave it to me to return to Plectrude."

Such rings borne by messengers often served to identify the messenger to people who couldn't read. This was the secret of the magic of Plectrude's ring; it identified Osric as being the envoy of the regent.

"But where is Osric now?"

Childebrand grunted. "Who knows? By this time he may be halfway back to Britain."

Very emphatically Charles instructed his brother to bring to him at once any news of this man. It was important that Osric be found.

To Childebrand, Osric had seemed to be an ordinary monk, one with odd ways, perhaps, but one met many like him every day in the week. Nevertheless, if Charles wanted this man found, Childebrand would make it his business to find him.

The hundred and twenty-odd miles to Metz was a matter of several days of hard riding. The company crossed the Moselle and continued southwest; the speed of their journey was possible only by reason of the good road.

About sundown of the third day, the cavalcade rode into Metz. The city was wedged tightly into the fork of the Moselle and the Seille rivers. Originally, it had been fortified by the Romans, who had built an aqueduct to supply it with water. Later, after successive attacks by the Vandals and the Huns, the Franks managed to repair the damage with their own kind of patchwork. Yet despite the fact that the Franks had no real skill for building, there was a feeling of security about the place because of its location.

Charles' company made its way to the "Palatium," the name given by the Gallic peoples to the great hall of their leaders. It was a combined court and residence—usually a former Roman public building which had withstood the ravages of time and war. The word *palace,* of course, comes from the "Palatine Hill," in Rome, where, sadly enough, the "palaces" of long dead emperors were even now crumbling away.

When Charles reached the door of Plectrude's palace, he became aware of a feverish bustle and scurry by people who seemed to lack any purpose or direction. The guards stepped aside, reluctantly, as Charles, in the company of his brother, entered the hall. The sense of confusion Charles had noticed outside was in evidence here, too, but he was also aware of certain quiet, purposeful men who were obviously waiting for something to happen. As they saw him, each one started to move toward him.

Just then, however, Charles was approached by one of the *domestici* who told him that Plectrude was awaiting him. As he neared the entrance of her apartment these silent men followed, but halted just outside the door. Charles recognized many of them, of course, and knew them to be *freiholdes,* or landholders, and their vassals, who had combined to use their influence to liberate Pepin's son, that he might lead them in this time of conflict.

Plectrude looked up as Charles entered. The air was heavy with the unspoken thoughts and feelings of all present. Her ministers were in full attendance, and in view of their numbers the silence was truly remarkable. Plectrude was never too far away from her advisors at any time, and since the advice of each had a tendency to differ from that of the next man, no decisions were reached, no action resulted, and paralysis of the nation had followed. The woman's self-doubt showed in her face and attitude; it was deepened by her fear of Charles. The councilors, too, showed this same fear. On the other hand, in this day and age, when vengeance and torture were common occurrences, Plectrude showed perhaps great fortitude by being present at all.

"Where is Rotruda?" were Charles' first words.

Plectrude explained rather hurriedly that Rotruda had not been feeling well; she had remained at home with the boys.

Charles' eyes glittered. His color was high.

"Very well. I will visit them presently. Now, my lady, what is your pleasure concerning me?"

The woman's eyelids fluttered; she looked at her retainers as if expecting help from that quarter. No one moved.

"The nobles of Austrasia have made their will clear," she said. "It is a time of war and trouble, Charles. I have agreed with them that Austrasia has need of a strong man to unite the country in the common cause. The *freiholdes* wish me to retain the regency while you, as duke of the army, cope with our enemies in the field."

Charles' glance flashed over the faces of all

those present; the councilors stirred restlessly. Many actually winced.

"May I speak with you alone, madame?"

Plectrude flushed and moistened her lips. Her mouth opened as if to say something, but no sound came. Finally she looked at her staff and nodded, and the men filed from the chamber without protest.

Alone in the room with Plectrude, Charles laid down his terms with force and clarity. In taking command of the army, he would ask for a personal oath of fealty from the barons to himself as Duke of Austrasia, with full military powers. His second point was no less explicit. In view of what had happened in the past, he was removing Plectrude from power as regent. In addition, she and her children would be under house arrest for as long as seemed necessary.

Plectrude tearfully protested Charles' stern orders, reminding him that when he was in prison she had been lenient with him.

A little hysterically she said, "Have you forgotten Grimoald? How will you bring Grimoald back, Charles?"

"There never was any proof of who Grimoald's assailants were. Nor those of Lambert, madame. Have you forgotten Lambert? He, too, is worthy of your tears!"

"Grimoald was my son, Charles. He was to have succeeded me as mayor of the palace. Lambert was not my flesh and blood. I have never

forgotten that you were away at the time of my
son's death. Rotruda—" She bit her lip.

"What about Rotruda?" snapped Charles. "I
only know that Grimoald's assassins were never
found. Shortly afterwards I went to prison. No
one could prove that I had had anything to do
with it, either, but to prison I went. What had
Rotruda to do with this?"

By this time Plectrude was weeping quite open-
ly and could not answer him.

"I am aware of your leniency toward me in
prison." Charles' tones were level. "After all, I am
here! But what is to be my assurance, as I take my
place in the field, that you won't change your
mind? If, for example, one of your ministers be-
comes fearful of me, will I be returned to prison?
In the event that the enemy is quickly defeated,
will I be banished so that I will not be in the
way when peace is restored?

"No, madame. I have made other plans. You
believe yourself to be a good mother to your children. Take care of them, then, but leave my
hands free to deal with the problems that con-
front Austrasia. I will not interfere with you, I
promise you, but I cannot have you free to interfere with me."

After he had seen Plectrude escorted to her
quarters by several of her serving women, he
returned to the great hall outside. On seeing
Charles again, with a look of triumph on his face,
the nobles roared their approval. In the ensuing

ceremonies which made Charles, Duke of Austrasia, leader of the country in time of war and supreme commander of the army, each of the barons, kneeling before him, swore an oath of personal fealty. The torchlight fell on joyful faces; faces on which had been drawn lines of tension and worry now shone with relief. Here was a man of stature, a natural leader of men proven in battle, clear in his mind and vigorous in his action. Of this they were certain.

In the bustle of mobilization, Charles found time to protect himself and his position from those in the country who had not shown their approval of his coming to power. Into the hands of one of his old comrades-in-arms Charles placed certain funds. A simple system was set up by which information of all kinds was brought quickly to Charles' attention. Once he could report victories to the people his position would be assured. In the meantime he would make sure that he knew at all times what was going on in all quarters. His brow darkened when he recalled how he had been awakened in the middle of the night by men whose faces he could not see and smuggled off to prison. This, he told himself, would never happen again!

Quickly, Charles set up his own staff to make sure that even after he had left for the campaigns all would move smoothly in his absence. He moved into Plectrude's chambers, which she had used as an office as well as her living rooms, and set up his headquarters. Plectrude herself was still in the building so that he was able to keep an eye on her movements, but, except for the surveillance, she and her children were decently treated.

By this time, Charles was fairly convinced of Plectrude's sincerity, but he realized that among her followers were many who had not received the news of his assumption of power with the same joy that the nobles had shown. Plectrude had friends, he knew, who had worked with her in her efforts to ease the lot of her people. Perhaps some of these might feel strongly about a new leader who might be disposed to bring an end to Plectrude's labors.

Charles therefore dismissed the palace staff and installed one which he selected with care. The first official to be replaced was the seneschal, a man of great authority. Plectrude's man had served Charles' father Pepin; the word seneschal simply means "elder servant," and certainly this man was the elder servant in every sense of the word. Yet even here, Charles did not hesitate. Since this official had charge of all meat and drink and had authority over all servants, Charles made sure that his new seneschal would not only be trustworthy himself but would actively prevent any tampering with the food by politically ambitious people!

In a like manner, Charles selected a new "count of the stables." This was the man who was responsible for the horses, their care and feeding and their breeding. He was the master of transport, so to speak. To him reported the marshals, or "masters of the horse." (Later on these titles would be spelled as constable and marshal, which have a very different meaning.)

In the days spent riding in the company of the paladins, Charles inspected the new levies as they marched in. The paladins and nobles, solidly made up of Charles' old comrades-in-arms, well-mounted and equipped, would form the core and center of the new army. Duke Charles built his army as well as he knew how, but there still seemed to be something lacking.

One evening late, after he and Childebrand had received and dismissed countless officials, envoys, and office-seekers, Charles suddenly said, "Find out about the Roman legions who once had their stations here. Find out how they were armed and trained, but most of all, find out why they were feared."

Childebrand was perfectly willing to do his brother's bidding, but he was puzzled by the request. After all, Charles' word was law, but where could one find out about such things? Charles spoke of maps and charts, but no one around the palace had ever seen them. Where had the duke picked up these notions? Perhaps something had happened to him while he was in prison. Charles seemed changed in other ways, too.

After musing about it for days, Childebrand

Charles inspected the new levies.

ventured to ask his brother where such information might be found.

"Inquire of those who can read and write. The records of such things *must* be found!"

Childebrand inquired among the clergy, but few even of this group could read and write. Who had records of books? Who had knowledge of these things?

And so as the fresh troops marched in, the Duke of Austrasia eyed them with discontent. They would be trained in the usual fashion, of course, but it wasn't quite enough. In Charles' mind there marched a different type of soldier. This soldier he had never seen, but his reputation for valor had outlived him for over three hundred years. During his lifetime few would dare to attack him, Osric had said. Give me a force like this, Charles vowed, and I will bring peace to Austrasia. Once again there would be cleared fields and great cities.

It was a vision which would never leave him, even though the Roman soldier was gone forever.

There was another matter which kept Charles awake at night. This was the business of securing clear, concise information about the enemy and his movements. Much time had been spent in questioning such people as peddlers, runaway slaves, pilgrims, beggars, merchants, and others of all kinds. War leaders had always made sure to question those left in the wake of a battle.

"Tell us all you can of what happened to your village," Charles would say.

A startled look would come into the eyes of the peasant. He would stare around at the faces of those in the room, scratch his head and cough or snuffle.

"Why, master, it's just that our village was burnt and our fields laid waste. Oh, ay, and those not quick enough to hide in the forest were led away captive."

"Who were the enemy? What people were they?"

The man's dull face usually showed no comprehension. With much head-shaking he would look at his wife and children. In stony silence they would stare back.

"Well, from what direction did they come, man?" a young scribe might ask.

Vaguely, the man would nod in a northerly direction.

"The Saxons, surely—the Frisians!" Murmurs of others were heard.

"But we don't know that for certain!" By this time Charles' patience would be gone. "Any army can come from any direction for any reason. We must have better information than this!"

For weeks he had been plagued by all sorts of half-truths, rumors, and downright distortions. One report had it that Ragenfrid, mayor of the palace of Neustria, had sent to the Duke of Aquitaine for help. Others said that troops from Aquitaine had already reached Paris. Another, that the Burgundians were also on the march—and then, the Burgundians were *not* on the march. The Frisians and Saxons had crossed the Rhine but had contented themselves with burning and looting. Other rumors insisted that the German tribes were massing for a blow at Cologne.

Charles realized he must have more accurate information about the plans of the opposing forces. A system was set up and action taken not only to keep the enemy in the field under constant observation but to put men into high places in the enemy camp in order to know their plans in advance. In this way, Charles expanded his area of intelligence.

The hammers of the smiths and metalworkers rose and fell, their ringing notes filling the night as well as the day with their clamor. Steadily the bellows pumped, keeping the fires hot; there were swords to be forged, chain mail to be repaired, spearheads and javelins to be made.

Charles had sent his messengers to all the villages and towns which had not yet sent their quota of troops. The local counts or margraves were ordered to muster their men immediately. So great had been the confusion under Plectrude's regency that many districts had been mobilized for some time while others had worked on in the fields hardly aware that anything was going on.

Most of the troops had been armed by the local

smiths in their own hamlets and villages, but some had been sent with the scantiest of weapons. Charles saw to it that each man was provided with a pike or javelin, a dagger or sword, and a round shield covered with hide or wood. A number had helmets, but there was no body armor for the foot soldier. Since the Franks had been woodsmen for generations, many of the men brought the axes they used in cutting down trees. The type of ax used for throwing was called a *francisca* and was developed by the Franks as a weapon. Perhaps from this weapon would come, one day, Charles' own sobriquet of "The Hammer."

Since these men were freemen—slaves were not used—each man expected to be back on the farm by harvest time. Duke Charles knew he would have to complete his campaign by then, so that the fewer preparations that were needed, the better. There would be no wagons for supply; the army would simply forage for its food. For pay for the troops, there was either plunder or not, according to the circumstances.

The Duke of Austrasia, during the hectic days of raising an army, kept pretty well to his companions-in-arms, or *fideles*. Many times Charles simply flung himself down on a pallet behind a curtain in his office to finish out a night mostly spent in wrestling with his problems; he ate with whatever official he happened to be consulting at mealtime.

Added to all the activity, casual visitors wandered in to tell a dream, or offering perhaps to tell a fortune. Such dreams or fortunes were given great importance in those days of deep superstition. Charles could not afford to ignore these visitors, for often the predictions had to do with the outcome of the approaching campaign. On the other hand, there were priests and abbots with problems of discipline; life went on, war or no war, and these were the stewards who would look after the people while the men were away with the armies.

With a deft sure touch, Charles brought all the factors together, and as confusion was eliminated, a strong weapon began to take form, the newly recreated army of Austrasia. On only one point did Charles falter, in only one particular did he run into a dead end. In all his efforts to bring about a reconciliation with his wife it was as if a black shadow had fallen across his family, through which he could see nothing. His patience at an end, one day, he said,

"As your husband, I must insist that you explain yourself. For over a year I have been unjustly imprisoned by a—"

The strange fear in her eyes deepened.

"Unjustly, Charles?" she said.

He was stunned. "Then you believe with Plectrude that I had something to do with Grimoald's death!" His voice rose. "So this is the way she strikes back at me—through my family! She—"

"Plectrude has done nothing, Charles. You have been away for a long time. Before you go away again, perhaps you should visit Alpaïde."

Charles did visit his mother, but again the trail led into deep shadows. Both women seemed to be concealing something, and there was nothing he could do about it.

With what savage relief did Charles welcome the sound of the trumpets calling upon the army to march!

CHAPTER THREE

Mayor of the Palace

The Austrasian host issued from Metz at dawn, crossed the Moselle, and moved in the general direction of the Ardennes. By early afternoon, the men were still pouring from the city. These troops did not march; they were not formed in tight ranks moving in step by squads and companies. They straggled in a rough column according to their villages, under the standards of their local counts, with laughter and jest after the manner of all fighting men of the time.

Charles, with several thousand horseman under the command of the paladins, was in the van, but the Frankish army was mainly one of infantry. Little use was made of cavalry, as such; the horsemen were the men of Charles' own personal army, and in days to come would be called knights. Each man wore a shirt of mail and a helmet and carried a buckler and lance. In addition, each wore a sword and a long knife for hand-to-hand combat. Since these men were soldiers by profession, they formed the nearest thing in Austrasia to a standing army.

At almost the same time the troops of Cologne, a hundred and twenty miles to the north, were also leaving their city. Later a junction would be made between these men and Charles' troops, but now the orders were to find the enemy.

Only burned villages and ravaged fields appeared to the men of Cologne; the marauders themselves were never seen, strangely enough. From the south Charles' forces pushed through the Ardennes Forest without flushing a single scout or patrol. At night, however, the troops bedded down with the feeling that at all times they were being watched. In the following days, although they kept a sharp lookout as they felt their way along the forest trails, the feeling persisted. And still, at no time had any of the flankers come upon a single enemy. Even though the Franks were born to the woods, the situation began to get on the men's nerves.

Charles listened to the reports of his scouts and videttes at torchlit councils, and the paladins shook their heads.

"Nothing," the seneschal was saying, "nothing is left. Whenever we come upon a hut or village, everything has been taken, everything burned. If it weren't for the game in the forest, our plight would be serious."

Only burned villages and ravaged fields appeared.

On the march, it was the duty of the seneschal to send his men ahead to seize food and supplies so that everything would be prepared by the time Charles rode up with his paladins and officials. However, with hunting parties combing the woods, game became more and more scarce; with an army on the march, even wells and springs dry up and the grumbling begins. The men who had served against the German tribes in the past recognized the touch of the Saxons and Frisians. Their evasive tactics never changed, not even here. The only question was at what time of day or night would these barbarians swarm at them from all directions.

The Austrasians issued from the forests in a pouring rain and moved northward into the Meuse Valley. It was now understood that they would meet the Cologne contingent at either Aix or Herîstal. Meanwhile, there was still no sign of the enemy, although the northern wing began to encounter small bands of Austrasian defenders, who, roughly handled by the Germans, had fallen back, regrouped, and fallen back again. These bands, having lost everything in their burned villages, were trying to harass the enemy by delaying raids. They could not hope to turn back the tide, but they did seek to do all the damage they could.

Messengers from the army of Cologne reported to Charles that the troops had halted at Liège on the way to Herîstal and would await him there.

Liège, a small town in those days at the junction of the Meuse and the Ourthe rivers, was actually the better meeting point. The messengers also reported that on the way to join Charles' forces they had observed a large number of troops who looked to be Neustrians, from the west. They had not verified this, since they were in a hurry, but the number of these troops was too large to be Austrasian partisans.

Charles passed the word to his own commanders and ordered Childebrand to take a body of mounted men, contact the unidentified army, and keep it under observation.

"Report to me regularly and let me know if they change their direction," he said.

The messengers further related that the strangers had also entered the Meuse Valley and were somewhere up ahead. The river flows northeast at this point, and Charles' men were proceeding in the same direction behind them. "Do not attack," was the order. "Simply keep them in sight. Do you understand?"

Childebrand grumbled. There were so many in his troop who were longing to come to grips with the enemy.

"What am I to tell these lads when they learn there is to be no challenge?"

Charles scowled; he seized his brother by both shoulders.

"Again I tell you that you are not to attack. Also, if you are attacked, withdraw at once!"

"My brother, how can I promise you this? You and I know these men. With such an order as that, I will have the whole company about my ears like a swarm of bees!"

The men were assembled in the rain, and Charles spoke to them as a stern father. By the time he had finished, there were many red faces among them.

His plan was simple. The troops from Metz were to follow along down the valley behind the enemy. In due course, the enemy would come upon the Austrasians lying at Liège. When the battle was joined, Charles would simply wait until the enemy was completely engaged and then move in on their rear and close the trap. His own troops might be said to be the hammer; the Austrasians at Liège would form the anvil; and the enemy would simply be crushed between them.

It was a good plan but unfortunately Charles was not leading a trained and disciplined army. He was aware that his men were more likely to obey orders if they happened to agree with their commander's judgment. To win renown as an individual fighting man was the only concept that made sense to a Frank.

Childebrand had disappeared into the mists with his horsemen, and in due time one of them returned to confirm the opinion of the messengers that the unknown force was indeed Neustrian. If they continued in their present direction they would encounter the Austrasians at Liège in a day or so. Duke Charles had already sent his *missi,* or messengers, to alert his people at Liège and the whole picture seemed too good to be true. If all went as planned, the Neustrians would be crushed in the first engagement, after which the united armies of Austrasia could simply run the Germans back across the Rhine.

Unfortunately, Childebrand lost control of his men. A mere handful, actually, insisted on charging the enemy's back; most of them returned safely since they had the advantage of surprise. However, this meant that the presence of Childebrand and his men was made known to the Neustrians. Not only did they find themselves pursued, but the whole Neustrian force faced about and started toward Charles' troops. When the two armies came together at Amblève, south of Liège, the collision took place.

Visibility was poor because of the weather and both sides made mistakes continually. This was Charles' first battle as a commander; through no fault of his own he was engaged with his whole force while ample reinforcements were lying at Liège wholly out of reach!

The battle raged back and forth for a time with the outcome in doubt, but when a fresh body of troops came suddenly out of the rain to reinforce the Neustrians, Charles was face to face with disaster.

Austrasian trumpeters sounded the retreat, although, in places, the duke was having to cope with a rout. His only desire now was to reach the security of the forests where he might regroup and reorganize his forces. Also, he intended to deal with some disobedient warriors!

Once in the shelter of the forest, another surprise was in store for the battle-weary Austrasians. Prisoners whom they had dragged after them were found to be men of Aquitaine, who had made up a contingent under the personal command of Odo, their duke! They had arrived on the scene late, having followed the Neustrian forces eastward in their search for their Saxon and Frisian allies.

Charles was in a fury. Not only had some of his paladins disobeyed his orders, but the very men who were to have kept him informed of the enemy's presence had failed him. Nor had there been any investigation, apparently, of the rumors that Aquitaine had entered the war on the side of Neustria.

From the shelter of the forest, Charles dispatched man after man to Liège to hasten the arrival of his reinforcements. Skies were clearing somewhat; if the visibility improved, something might yet be saved from the wreckage.

In a forest clearing, Charles dealt swiftly with the disobedient horsemen who had attacked the Neustrians. The scene between Childebrand and Charles was particularly grim.

"You were told to restrain your men!" Charles said in a voice that shook with passion, "and this you failed to do! By revealing our presence to the enemy you and your men have brought defeat upon the whole army!" He struggled to control himself and then said, "I have no room in this army for such as you." Turning, he walked away into the shadows.

The Austrasians slept on their weapons that night, and when day came, Childebrand had gone, together with his followers.

The campaign dragged on in a welter of disorganized actions without Charles ever being able to bring the situation to a head. Ragenfrid, mayor of the palace of Neustria, and Odo of Aquitaine had joined in time to catch Charles off-balance and drive him deeper into the Ardennes Forest. Later, Austrasian forces, having run all the way from Liège, arrived in time to take enemy attention off Charles for a while. The men of Metz poured out of the forest, but when night fell, both sides lay down, keeping each other in sight, or so it seemed. In the morning, Ragenfrid, Odo, and their men had stolen away. There was no enemy in sight in any direction.

By the time winter ended the campaign, Charles had secured the situation, but he was far from satisfied with his accomplishment, his army, or his position. Most of his men had already straggled home to get in the crops; the stalemated war was kept alive only by the professional soldiers on both sides keeping each other in view.

Suddenly Charles was overcome by a feeling

that there was no more time to loose. Leaving his troops wintering in the Ardennes Forest, he hurried to Metz.

Plectrude, busy with her household tasks in her suite at the palace, was greatly startled one day shortly afterward when one of her serving women told her that the Duke Charles was at the door. He had asked to see her. As she looked up, Charles walked in, unbidden.

She saw his travel-stained cloak, the lines of tension and fatigue about his mouth and eyes, and his wind-burned skin.

"You look tired, Charles," she said.

"I wanted to talk to you."

Plectrude toyed with the urge to make a scathing remark, thought better of it, and said,

"Well?"

"The war in the north is being contained," he said. "It should hold until spring. However, I have been thinking of our position in Metz. Until the enemy has been finally dealt with, I shall be in the field. In the meantime, the throne of Austrasia is vacant."

Plectrude laughed mirthlessly.

"Don't tell me that you are already reaching out to claim the throne, too, Charles." She laughed again. "It always begins the same way, I am told. First, command of the army, then to take over the rulership of the country." Her voice rose in her bitterness. "And what is to stop you,

Charles, from taking anything you want? Why speak to me?"

Charles flushed, but he retained control.

"I had not thought of the throne for myself. The people need a symbol—a figurehead to look up to—someone of the line of Meroveus, whose royal blood bears the tradition not only of Austrasia but of Neustria as well. I had Clotaire in mind."

"Well, and what about you?"

"Mayor of the palace, naturally," he said, nodding as if no other possibility existed.

The Merovingian line of kings had begun with the legendary Meroveus, or "Son of the Sea." As the Franks had become a forest people, their tradition of the sea had become lost to memory. Later, under Clovis and his queen Clotilda, the Burgundian, the forest people had become Christianized as a nation, but their Christianity was a strange mixture of the new teachings and the old superstitions. The Merovingian kings had been hero kings in the German tradition, but, as generations passed, they became weak and ineffectual, fit only to be the empty symbols of past glories.

Neustria, which means the "Western Land," and Austrasia, the "Eastern Land," had come about through the custom of Frankish kings dividing their realm, upon their death, among their sons. This division always resulted sooner or later in confusion and disunity.

The real power of the kingdoms of Neustria

and Austrasia now lay in the hands of the so-called "mayors of the palace." This official had originally been like the manager of a great estate. He handled all the affairs of the palace; he arranged meetings between the king and his nobles; and he was the go-between in the affairs of state. After King Dagobert's time, however, the mayor of the palace took over more and more of the royal duties as the kings became weaker. At last he managed not only the affairs of the palace but of the whole kingdom as well!

So it was that Charles, son of Pepin, now proposed to step into the position his father had held, mayor of the palace.

"And what about me?" Plectrude asked. "Am I to go on living here, a virtual prisoner, being spied on and supervised, never to go out unless someone goes with me, who will be sure to report all I have said? Is this what you have in mind?"

"No, my lady, I had thought to mention certain changes that had occurred to me." Charles seated himself and sighed with weariness. "I had thought of a pleasant place for you to live, free from surveillance, free to be with your children, to play with your grandchildren—in other words, to live the life of a woman as it was intended."

"This means, I suppose, that I must take an oath of fealty to you," Plectrude said bitterly. "For this, you will allow me to live the life of a woman 'as it was intended,' as you describe it. But what of my life as regent, Charles? Are all the plans I

"And what about me?" Plectrude asked.

had made to improve the lot of the freemen to be forgotten?"

Charles was aware of Plectrude's hopes to bring about better conditions for the peasants. He had similar plans to be developed along slightly different lines. Suddenly he laughed. It would be his pleasure, he said, to work with her on such plans after the war was won, and in peace he could set the kingdom in order again.

If Charles had need to forgive and forget his term in prison, Plectrude no less needed to rid herself of suspicions—which she could not prove —as to the assassin of Grimoald, her son. For Plectrude to see Charles holding the office of mayor of the palace, a position which under happier circumstances Grimoald would be holding now, would always be a painful experience for her. For Charles to overlook deliberately the humiliation and frustration of spending a year of his life in prison was the mark of a man of stature. Both must try to put aside their grievances for the good of their country.

Trumpets sounded now in Metz as the coronation of Clotaire IV was proclaimed to the people. The crown was placed on his head by the Bishop of Metz, and all drew near to do homage to the royal name. Very little else about Clotaire was worthy of honor, however. Young, vacuous of mind, soft of body, he rode through the streets in the traditional wagon drawn by oxen and led by a peasant. In his reviews, he saw the envoys and officials and answered their petitions as he had been told. However, for better or worse, this was the king, and the people accepted him as their nominal ruler. His rule was a brief one without importance, unworthy of note, to insure only that the Austrasian throne was occupied.

At the same time, Charles was officially made mayor of the palace, which meant that any important royal edicts would originate with him. Clotaire would merely sign the documents.

In the spring, Charles and his paladins again took the field to bring to a victorious conclusion the campaign begun the year before. Charles felt Childebrand's loss greatly, but during the winter he had had time to think things through. Frankish warriors, instead of counting on victory through sheer heroism, were going to learn what it meant to obey. A handful of men had disobeyed a single order and chaos had resulted. This was a great lesson learned by Charles at Amblève. This, too, would never happen again!

Now the men of Cologne were moving northward along the Rhine to seal off the Frisians and Saxons. Under cover of this wing, Charles, with the troops made up of the men from the Metz area, turned sharply west for a thrust at Paris, capital of Neustria. Again the smoke of burning villages was seen as the Neustrians retreated before him.

Reports arrived during this time which told

that the Burgundians had decided against entering the war on the side of Neustria. If Neustria and Aquitaine were victorious, then Burgundy could make her bid for independence. Charles realized that he would have to be quick about bringing the war to a successful conclusion, for if he fumbled the campaign now, he could expect to face a possible uprising by the Burgundians.

Scouts and spies reported that Ragenfrid was assembling a large force at Cambrai. A smaller force, under Odo of Aquitaine, barred the road to Paris. The plan was to allow Charles to attack Odo's men, who would fall back. Once Charles was well on his way to Paris, the larger army from Cambrai would move south and lock the door behind him.

When this information had been verified, Charles moved fast. With his horsemen leading the way, the Austrasians broke through Odo's line as intended. However, the bulk of the army wheeled northward. They came upon the Neustrian army as it was fording a stream near Vincy.

The surpise was so complete that a general panic ensued. As Ragenfrid's army scattered, the back of the rebellion was broken. Odo attempted to come to Ragenfrid's aid and arrived on the spot just in time to take part in the surrender.

Hostages were taken, the Neustrian and Aquitanian troops were disarmed, and all security measures carried out. In an expansive gesture,

Charles treated Ragenfrid as if he were receiving an old friend whom he had not seen for a long time. Perhaps the sight of the mayor of the palace of Neustria, dripping muddy water while he gave his oath, appealed to Charles' sense of humor. More likely, since Charles was already planning to reunify both kingdoms of Frankland, as a first step it was necessary to erase all bitterness as quickly as possible. He had no such feeling toward the Aquitanians, however, and as for the Burgundians—he had special plans for them!

The next step was to reinforce the Austrasians in the north, who were hard at work hammering the Frisians and Saxons back to their own side of the Rhine. At almost the same time, plans were put into action for the rebuilding of the villages which had been destroyed.

The victorious banners of Austrasia floated over Soissons later that same year. To this city the nobles came to witness the signing of a peace treaty between Ragenfrid of Neustria, Odo of Aquitaine, and Ragenbod of the German allies on the one hand, and Charles on the other. It was a fitting spot to raise the pavilions for such a meeting; here the young Clovis I had defeated Syagrias, the Roman governor of the district and accepted the surrender of the last Roman garrison. In the same spirit of triumph, Charles took the first step in bringing Neustria and Austrasia together again to form one nation. After all, both nations were Frankish; they belonged together. The

Aquitanians and the Burgundians, on the other hand, were of Gallo-Roman stock, a different people.

In order to show his intentions, Charles settled an earldom upon Ragenfrid. It was Anjou with its capital at Angers. He encouraged fraternizing, too, between the Franks of both sides; it would be necessary for the two peoples to get to know each other. He would do everything to enable the Neustrians to regain their pride, and he would take every step to bind up the wounds incurred in the war.

At no time, however, would Charles attempt to hurry the healing process. Time was needed for this.

Not far from the Abbey of Notre Dame, the pavilion for the signing of the peace had been erected. On all sides stood the nobles to witness the signing; there stood the Aquitanians in their Romanized dress beside the shaggy Germans from their dismal swamps in the north, impassive Austrasian paladins, and clergy of all ranks. Charles straightened up from placing his mark upon the documents prepared by the scribes. His eye fell upon a tall, spare, soldierly figure standing some distance away. This was Odo, Duke of Aquitaine, imperial in his bearing and magnificent in his arrogance.

Odo was about fifty years old at this time; his grey hair and beard were worn long as if he were of royal blood. His cloak and tunic were immacu-

late, and everything about him was of the Roman
fashion.

Charles walked slowly over to him and stood
looking into his eyes. Those around them held
their breath. At times like these, Charles' eyes became mere pinpoints of light; those who knew
Charles feared for anyone at whom Charles leveled that look. There was that evening at Amblève when armed Aquitanians broke through
curtains of rain and mist to hurl themselves on
the exhausted Austrasians and beat them back
into the forest. By this stroke, Odo had taken a
hand in what Charles considered a strictly Frankish affair. And now here he stood numbered
among the vanquished, completely in Charles'
power. It was a sweet moment!

The older man looked back into Charles' eyes
and smiled his contempt. It was like a blow in the
face.

Charles' chin lifted slightly. He could be gener-
ous to a beaten foe, but the time would come
when Odo would learn to fear Charles more than
the Saracens!

CHAPTER FOUR
The Field of Mars

Now the Burgundians could hear the war hymns of the victorious Franks as they made their way down the Saône Valley. Next, above the tree-tops, appeared dust clouds kicked up by many thousands of feet, and finally came the men themselves. Numbers of them bore fowls or pigs slung over their lances; they were in high spirits, moving with the swagger born of their confidence in their leader.

Swiftly they passed through such towns as Besançon, Vienne, Lyon, and Avignon, stopping only to accept tribute offered by the local counts and bishops and to exact pledges and take hostages. In the Rhone Valley, the lesson was clearly spelled out that a man who could move so quickly with an army was no man to have for an enemy. And yet, in accepting tribute from the worried

Burgundians, Charles spoke words of gentle reasonableness.

"A nation of fragments," he explained, "has little claim to greatness. In war, the enemy swallows each *civitas* in turn, and in trade, there are boundaries to pass and tributes to pay. One district will hunger while another lives in fatness. A thousand small armies guard each border; no man is free to plant or harvest his crop without the bickerings which follow, while the smoke goes up from burning villages!

"I offer you the protection and guarantees that a unified people can offer its citizens. Make no mistake, the Franks and their people will rule because we have settled the differences between us and face our enemies as one people!"

The Burgundian counts and bishops looked at each other and agreed that this young man might be speaking perfect truth! Bishoprics were tendered as guarantee for Burgundian conduct; only when this had been done did the Franks leave. However, long after the troops had disappeared into the distance, the Burgundians remembered how quickly Charles had been able to reach them. This lesson would influence their decisions for a long time to come.

From the banks of the Loire, Charles now summoned Duke Odo of Aquitaine to a meeting. The steel in his voice was maintained by the presence of an Austrasian army strung out along the Loire ready for an instant march into Aqui-

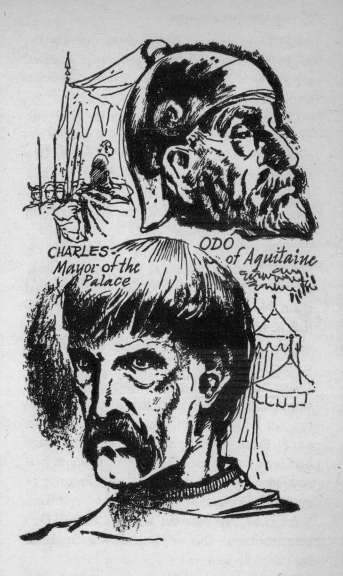

CHARLES
Mayor of the
Palace

ODO
of Aquitaine

taine. There was something about the way the bright sun shone on the spearheads of Charles' army which convinced Odo that the situation could change at any moment.

Charles' pavilion was set up on the riverbank overlooking Aquitanian soil. From across the river came the men of Aquitaine, their leader Odo immaculate as usual in his Roman style of dress. The trumpets sounded, the ceremonies and speeches followed, and then came the business at hand. Charles wasted no words.

"In Burgundy, the nobles and the bishops were as one in their expressions of loyalty to the Frankish crown. All expressed their joy at being united again. Now we are here to learn what your position is. In the past, Aquitaine has governed herself with a large measure of freedom. It shall so remain if you desire it."

Odo, a man of the world, seasoned in the art of war and experienced in affairs of state and politics, felt his color mounting swiftly. This upstart son of Pepin II, who only a few short years ago had been rotting in a dungeon in Cologne, was now about to ask him for an oath! Probably to guarantee Frankland's southern border by taking hostages, as if he were one of the half-naked German chieftains! This stripling! Young enough to have been his son, too!

Still, there had been Vincy—and later on, Soissons. . . .

"Just what do you require of me?" he found himself asking.

"Merely a guarantee of security for my borders on the Loire and a profession of friendship between us."

"And what is the price of your—er—friendship? What hostages are wanted? Name them."

"I want the person of Chilpèric II, King of Neustria."

Odo's eyes flickered slightly.

"I don't know what you mean."

"When you left Soissons"—Charles' tone was hard—"you took a hostage of your own. This may only have been to guarantee your northern borders, I realize." Odo flushed at Charles' sarcasm. "Now I want Chilpèric returned, at once," he said.

Odo realized he had no choice.

"Let it be as you say," he replied. "I shall give the order at once."

"And his treasure!" snapped Charles.

When the king, together with his considerable riches, had been liberated from Odo's custody, the Franks moved off in a northerly direction, and Odo returned to his capital in a towering rage. Charles restored Chilpèric to the Neustrian throne, which he occupied until his death the following year.

It was by such gestures that Charles made haste to woo the Neustrians, to obliterate as far as possible all the scars of war, and to give them equality as Franks in the eyes of their state.

Charles' people welcomed him home to Metz with bonfires and shouts of thanksgiving. He was a hero now in Frankish eyes, for his prowess had given them a taste for victories. The nobles flocked about him with fresh avowals of loyalty and service; his soldiers idolized him.

On the other hand, while Plectrude seemed to accept her new situation with fair grace, Rotruda remained aloof and remote.

Charles was still fretting and fuming over this situation, which not only separated them but threatened his ties with the boys as well, when suddenly Alpaïde sent for him. He went to see her and found her ailing and alone. To Charles, who preferred clear issues instead of mysteries, the matter of Grimoald's death was a thorn in his side. Much to his surprise and gratification, Alpaïde now revealed the truth. Bit by bit, as the story came out, he was able to understand why Plectrude had imprisoned him. It was an ugly story.

At a royal banquet Lambert, Bishop of Liège, had expressed his opinion of Alpaïde in no uncertain terms. He was followed to the episcopal mansion by Alpaïde's brother and there slain. Grimoald, son of Plectrude and heir to succeed her as mayor of the palace, had come there on a pilgrimage. Perhaps he had seen too much; at any rate, Grimoald's body was found nearby. Since the assassin had never been found—or the accom-

plices—Plectrude, although she could prove
nothing, had confined Charles as a safety measure!

Because Plectrude had never borne any love for
Alpaïde or her family, Alpaïde chose to remain silent. This allowed the brother to remove himself
from the vicinity while Charles went to prison. Alpaïde was sure that Plectrude would never put to
death a son of Pepin; whereas her brother would
probably not live long enough to stand trial. Later
on, perhaps, *wergeld,* or a fine, might bring about
Charles' freedom.

"I am telling you this, Charles," his mother said
in level tones, "since I have just had word that my
brother—your uncle—has died. Whatever he did,
Charles, he was the avenger of my honor." A long
silence followed. "Ah, well. Perhaps my time will
come soon also."

Such tragedies were anything but rare; con-
cepts like this of honor and duty were character-
istic of the warrior peoples. The heady legends of
the warrior gods set the pattern by which the people were fired to deeds of heroism and fortitude.
They also drove them into bloody acts of vengeance to wipe out real or fancied insults. Set
against all this was Christianity with its slow and
patient ways, but for a long time to come most of
the people of the world would continue to be
"warrior people."

In spring, the missi and heralds were sent forth
to all parts of the kingdom to proclaim a great

conventus of all the nobles. This was a meeting to
be held every year from now on in the month of
March—*Lenzinmanoth*—or the month of Lent;
or in June—*Wunnemanoth,* or "joy month," at
the latest. At this "Field of Mars," as it was called,
the mayor of the palace, in the presence of the
king, would announce his plans for the year to
come. At the same time, he would confer with the
nobles and bishops about any special problems.

Government by representatives of all the people
was many centuries away. These meetings were
of the nobles and clergy only; the peasants or the
freemen had no voice whatever. Charles would
simply address his followers and tell them what
he planned to do. The nobles had only to approve.

A central location was chosen for such a meeting in order to give everyone an equal distance to
travel insofar as possible. Rheims was the place;
Clovis I had been crowned there. For centuries to
come, French kings would be crowned in
Rheims. It had been there that a band of warriors
had been transformed into the beginning of the
kingdom of the Franks.

Since Charles' people were outdoor people, the
pavilions were set up in a place of rolling hills,
meadows, and trees, in an atmosphere of relaxa-
tion and joy. As the nobles and their followers
rode in from all directions, there was a feeling
that unity in the kingdom had at last been
achieved under a leader heroic enough for any
Frankish taste.

First, the king was presented in his ox-drawn wagon and duly honored. The nobles crowded about with their petitions, and the king answered them according to his instructions. Next came a review of the troops under the paladins, their pennants and standards making a brave showing. Games and individual feats of arms followed, and in this atmosphere there was a feeling of excitement that something new and worthwhile would be born here.

Now Charles, Duke of Austrasia, and mayor of the palace, prepared to address the assembly.

The plan that he outlined had been used, in a sense, a long time before this, but a clearer, more definite pattern was to be set up. The foundation and cornerstone of the new system was based on the proposition that every man should have a plot of land for his own use. It would supply the food for his family, but also it would be worth defending in time of war. The man without land had little interest in defending someone else's property. The *freiholdes,* or landholders, under the king, were bound to respect this basic right of their subvassals. Also, many landholders had been nimble enough in taking their share of each crop in payment for use of the land; from now on it would be the duty of the landholder to feed his people in time of famine. At this point in his address, Charles slapped the hilt of his sword.

When Charles casually announced that he had distributed a number of benefices to his paladins and commanders who had ridden into battle with him, there followed a deathly silence.

In the past, kings and nobles had disposed of their properties by turning over much land to the Church, but the use of the land had been granted to the former owner by the monastery. As a result, about one-third of the kingdom was in Church hands at this time. What Charles was saying was that he had seized a number of these benefices, or *praecariums,* and distributed them to his followers or allies.

The following day, Charles was waited on in his pavilion by a number of bishops and abbots. They pointed out that the holdings Charles had distributed to his followers had been Church property. Was Charles aware of this?

Charles looked at their earnest faces and smiled but said nothing.

One of the bishops went on to say that some of the Burgundian bishoprics had been turned over to German allies; besides this, there were soldiers who had been given Church positions. Milon, Archbishop of Trèves and Rheims, had been a soldier under Charles. What were his clerical qualifications?

Charles explained that he had need of able administrators. If a soldier had been given a Church post, it was because he had selected him for his proven ability. The priests and abbots in such a diocese could carry out their spiritual duties as always; there was no need for the head of a diocese to be more than a good administrator, Charles told them.

The audience went on for a long time. In fact, from many, Charles would never hear the end of it.

The bishops and abbots next pointed out that to remove Church treasure and confiscate Church property was a form of sacrilege. Had Charles ever thought of that?

Charles reminded them of how much property had been bequeathed to the Church throughout the years. By now it had become the treasure-house of the kingdom in secular things as well as spiritual. In order to bring about a strong new state and establish peace and order in Frankland, he had had to pay his armies and their commanders in some way. He had called upon the Church for help in carrying out this work, since the Church was the only source of treasure and currency in the kingdom. Where else could he go?

"My lord bishops," he declared, "if this is sacrilege, let it be on my head. Let my people be free of this transgression, since I am wholly responsible."

The troubled clerics withdrew, shaking their heads. Perhaps the term "sacrilege," applied to his use of Church funds, seemed to him extreme, but by his present efforts he was laying the foundation for what would one day be known as feudalism. Its purpose was to care for its subjects, with the nobles responsible to their king for their well-being, and the Church to oversee the weights and balances.

From the south now came new rumblings and alarums—trouble for Odo of Aquitaine. Couriers reaching Charles told of an invasion of Odo's domain by the Saracens, or Moors. These sons of the Prophet had issued from their stronghold of Narbonne and had driven on Toulouse, Odo's capital. Odo had managed to withdraw with most of his troops, but shut up in the city itself was its garrison and citizens in a state of siege.

Odo appealed to Charles for a meeting. The Duke of Aquitaine wanted a pact; it was clear to Charles that if Odo was being attacked in the south he would want to make sure that his back door in the north was securely bolted.

At this meeting of the year 720, the older man was tense and ill at ease; he was impatient to return to his beleaguered capital and the host of other problems that he faced. Gone was the cool, supercilious attitude of the previous years; no longer did the Aquitanian look down his nose at the upstart son of Pepin. Odo was very willing now to make his profession of friendship, but more than this he wanted a mutually signed pledge of peace.

On the other hand, the man who signed the document on behalf of himself and the Frankish nation was rather enjoying himself. He would be pleased to sign the pact with Odo and then see if

Odo could worm his way out of this combination of difficulties. In any case, he would keep his eye on Odo. After all, if Odo wasn't able to beat off the Saracens, Charles' own border might be endangered.

Strangely enough, however, with the pact signed and sealed, the Duke of Aquitaine mustered fresh troops and marched to the south with new spirit. The following year he raised the siege of Toulouse and soundly defeated the Saracens. Among the slain was Samh, the Saracen commander. Once again Aquitaine was free of its enemies.

Perhaps Charles had something to think about with this turn of events. While it was gratifying that Odo had been able to handle the situation without help, it was almost sure to make him more difficult to deal with in the future!

In Metz, the mayor of the palace turned his attention to other matters. The Bishop and his clerics called on Charles to inform him that a papal envoy was coming to Metz from Rome.

Wynfrith, a Saxon missionary of Britain, had worked for many years to bring Christianity to the Frisians, the Bavarians, and the Thuringians. Under Willibrord, another British Saxon and first Bishop of Utrecht, he had preached successfully for three years. Now, after a visit to Rome, Wynfrith had been made bishop by Pope Gregory II; he had been commissioned to return to Germany to continue his work on a larger scale. In Rome, he had been given the name "Boniface," the name by which he would always be remembered.

This man would stop at Metz on his way to Germany. Would Charles see him?

Charles had heard of Wynfrith. Travelers in Germany had reported that the missionary's path through the German forests could almost be traced by the new influences he had brought upon the people. Charles had certainly been aware of the influence of Christianity and its importance in his own country. The German tribes, for their part, could always be depended upon to rise up with fire and sword at any and all times. The miracle of the Anglo-Saxon missionaries was that the sons of Wotan and Thor would listen to them at all! It was imperative, therefore, for the Franks, in building a civilized state, to see to it that the Germans developed along the same lines at the same time.

Charles would be very happy to see Boniface and said so.

Boniface, they informed him, had letters from the Pope. Perhaps Charles' first thought was that the Pope's message might deal with the old matter of the benefices and the praecariums. There were abbots and bishops in Frankland who had never forgiven him for using Church property in times of emergency.

As Boniface entered the council chamber, Charles was first aware of the powerful sense of presence. Then came the feeling that he had met him before in the distant past. Next, he looked at him, noting the flowing hair and beard, the simple robe, and the travel-stained sandals. He marveled at this man who, without arms or an army, had gone among the German tribes to talk and preach to them, a people who had always considered war and violence the proper business of a man.

Strangely enough, this feeling awoke within him the memory of a monk who had visited him in a prison cell many years ago. He hadn't thought of Osric for a long time.

Pope Gregory's message to Charles, however, had nothing to do with the benefices and the praecariums. Instead it gave him the customary greeting of the Holy See and requested from Charles a letter of protection for Boniface on his new mission.

"The world knows of your valor as a soldier," the missionary said, almost at once, "and Rome has been watching your career with interest." He paused and his eyes twinkled. "Can it be that your sword is at the service of your Church?"

Charles smiled.

"Many years ago, Lord Bishop, I was visited by a certain monk who had also come from Rome." He laughed. "At that time, mind you, I had a very strong impression that Rome had been watching my career with interest. I've wondered why."

The two men seated themselves. In a way they were much alike; both were used to vigorous

This man had preached among the German tribes.

thrusts and counterthrusts at long odds. Each in his own way was a soldier; each in his own way was a missionary.

"Does that possibility seem strange to you?" Boniface asked. "Remember the Battle of Tolbiac, then, when Clovis called upon the God of his Christian queen, Clotilda, for aid. When the victory was his, he was baptized at St. Martin's in Paris and three thousand of his warriors with him. From that day onward, Frankland has been a Christian nation! Do you think the Church has ever forgotten that?

"Do you see now why the Holy See might have been watching your career with interest?"

A long pause followed.

"As a soldier," Charles mused, "I have found that work done with the sword must always be done over and over again. There is never any rest."

Boniface nodded, and then went on to explain his reason for asking for Charles' help. In his explanation he happened to mention the *Pax Romana,* by which a few legions strategically placed had, by their presence alone, maintained peace for two hundred years.

"And so it would be with you, Your Excellency." Boniface turned a radiant face to his host. "With the Frankish army poised on the Rhine ready to march, you would never have to draw your sword at all! Your presence would be enough! Don't you see?"

Charles flushed with excitement. For years he had admired the valor of the Roman legions and their power for peace. Now his own troops were being compared to them and he was being asked to employ them in a similar way.

"All that would be necessary," the missionary said, standing up, "would be an open letter to all whom I meet that Charles of Frankland is behind me in the work. It would be enough that the Saxons, the Frisians, the Alemanni, and the others know that. We are invoking the power of the written word"—again his eyes twinkled—"*not* the power of the sword!"

Nothing could have better fitted in with Charles' plans. With the German tribes quiet, there would be some possibility for the growth of his own people.

"Now that I have found a greater weapon," he said, "I shall look forward to a time when I can lay aside my sword." He thought for a moment and then shook his head quickly. "But that, I fear, is a long time away.

"In any case, I shall give instructions for the letters to be written at once."

CHAPTER FIVE

The Rule of the Frank

Boniface had crossed the Rhine and disappeared into the forests. At the same time Charles prepared for a journey also.

At the head of his paladins and nobles, he had made a number of journeys throughout the kingdom. The purpose of such trips was to make sure that the edicts laid down in the yearly meetings were carried out. In the past, during times of uprising and rebellion, Charles had shown how quickly he could reach any point in his realm with an army. By the same token, in times of peace, his counts and officials in the hamlets and villages never knew when their mayor of the palace was likely to put in an appearance. It was well to see that everything was in good working order at all times.

As a Frank, Charles was fond of the outdoors; to him it was the natural environment for a man.

Even through teeming rains and deep snow, these journeys brought peace to a man's soul. There were so many things of interest to see; there were always odd adventures and strange experiences to tell about at home when the journey was over. There was the time when, in pushing through a dense forest trail, they came upon the ruins of a village, forgotten, swallowed up in the undergrowth. Another time it was a ruined Roman villa, and in the heating system under the floor the men had found the skeleton of a slave still clutching the remains of a bag long turned to dust. About him lay gold coins. The enemy who had destroyed this villa had departed without ever finding the treasure of the slave who died to save it. Some of the nobles had in their houses water pipes which had been removed from ruins of Roman baths. There was no end to the marvels one might find.

In the forests, too, dwelt the scops, a flitting race of forest people who lived in hovels and were barely fed and clothed. Usually, they fled when approached, but when sufficient presents had been offered, these creatures might be persuaded to foretell the future, with their crude harps near at hand. Some of the men consulted the scops to find out if all was well at home, or when they would see their families again, or if a sweetheart had been true. The old ways of belief were not too far below the surface. Such missionaries as Boniface had encountered these superstitious practices often and dealt with them vigorously.

In coming out of the forest, it was pleasant to see the tilled fields and villages or to follow the road down into a town. The villages were made up of huts usually clustered along the bank of a stream and giving off the pleasant odor of their cooking fires.

The church was located a little way back from the road, and the manor house, where the local count lived with his family, was set a short distance apart. The sounds of the smithy could be heard from afar; the barking of dogs came later as the cavalcade drew nearer, and always there was the lowing of the cattle.

Everyone looked up as the long line of horsemen approached. The count, together with the priest, or perhaps the local abbot, came forth to welcome the visitors, and preparations were made to entertain them. Charles' seneschal stated their needs to the count's people, telling what was required by way of food and supplies; horses were shod at the smithy and repairs made on equipment and arms if necessary.

Charles usually stayed at the manor house or villa of the count. The villas in the Gallo-Roman parts of the country were almost as they had been in Roman days. Each contained a mill, a wine press, a forge, and an *a capella* oratory—where the first churches had begun.

The lord or seigneur was the governor of the district and held his tenure in the name of the king. He was also the supreme judge of the local *mallus,* or court, and had charge of collecting taxes, mustering troops in time of war, and overseeing crops. Since these lords and counts could, and very often did, abuse this power, Charles had been careful at his very first *conventus* to specify the rights and duties of each. The bishops were given the power to regulate the decisions of the count or noble if it was needed. In every case, the nobles and clergy were expected to look after their people; they were to be their shepherds and teachers.

At the great hall of an earl or count, Charles might ask the bishop to give thought to educating intelligent boys of the village at the parish schools. These schools were educating young people for the Church only, but Charles had need of scribes and administrators as well. Too few people could read or write; Charles himself made his mark on documents under the seal of the scribes. Later on, Charlemagne would try to teach people to read and write through his school, but even in his day there would be few educated men, even among the clergy.

After a day or so spent in a district Charles and his entourage would ride on. At each place visited, Charles would make sure that his officials carried out their duties according to the edicts and took care of the people, as he expected to look after his nobles and followers.

In the larger towns, the cavalcade might ride in on market day or during the time of a fair when people were in a festive mood. At other times, they might look on at a court trial when an offender was given a trial by ordeal. Since it was believed that if a person came through an ordeal uninjured or if his wounds healed within a certain time he was innocent, an accused man might be made to plunge his arm into a pot of boiling water, far enough to bring up a stone from the bottom. If the resulting burns showed signs of healing within three days, the man might be adjudged innocent.

One day Charles, on catching a man who held a duplicate stone in his hand when he plunged his arm into the water, ruled that henceforth a ring should be placed in the jar. "If this is to be an instrument of justice, then it must be carried out honestly," he ruled.

Other such trials might consist of walking across a bed of hot stones or trial by combat. In trial by combat, there would be no scarcity of witnesses in the areas where such exciting events were rare. In most of these towns no theater or arena had been known for generations, and the people were not treated to the spectacle of the thundering hoofs and breaking of lances that were always a joy to behold.

Most of the social life of these people, however, centered around Church festivals and sacramental services, where there was merrymaking afterwards. Minstrels and other entertainers were always welcome. In all these activities, Charles and his men played their parts in order to show the people that their mayor of the palace cared about them.

Wherever Charles went on these journeys, his court went also. The missi, who kept him informed of all that went on, came and went. There were disputes to settle, documents to sign, and information from all sources to be pieced together. Charles took along his scribes to read the dispatches to him and to write down his messages in reply.

From Boniface in Germany came messages of hope and optimism. Armed with his letters of protection by Charles, the zealous missionary had gone to the heart of matters as he saw them. Near Fritzlar, Boniface had "hewed down the 'Holy Oak' of the Hessians and no one lifted a hand to stop me!" It was almost his first act after leaving the court of Charles.

The act of cutting down a tribal tree was tantamount to smashing a people's idol before the high priests!

This tree was selected by a German tribe as a symbol of the tribe's own life. Rooted in the earth, its branches sheltered its children and, literally and figuratively, gave them something to look up to. It served as a rallying point in time of war, and under its branches councils were held. It was the sanctuary where the soothsayers told of the future and where blood sacrifices were offered. In years to come, Charlemagne was to discover such a tree to be the storehouse of the tribe's treasure.

An attempt at any other time to destroy such a tree would have been the signal for the tribe to rise up and fight until the last man, woman, and child were dead. To Charles, the importance of Boniface's message lay in the fact that, because of a letter he had written for Boniface's protection, a German tribe, in effect, had been disarmed.

"The power of the written word," Boniface had said.

With this demonstration, Boniface had made haste to summon monks and nuns from far-off Britain to help him in his work. What more proof of Charles' powers of protection could one want?

At the same time, Charles decided to follow up his promise to Boniface by a show of strength. This would be best understood by the Germans if he took hostages and tribute. They understood force and the power of the sword; indeed, anyone who did not understand this first law of life was merely weak and not worthy of notice, in their eyes. Strange it may have been to find British-Saxons carrying out the Christianization of their German-Saxon brothers, yet logical too. Who would understand the mind and heart of a Saxon better than another Saxon? The word Saxon means "long knife." Boniface and Willibrord would best understand what that meant.

And so, with his armed *fideles,* Charles moved

into the German forest along the trails blazed by
Boniface and his helpers. As he expected, where-
ever the people had accepted Christianity a dis-

Charles moved in the trails blazed by Boniface.

tinctly different pattern had emerged. Small
churches were appearing on newly cleared land.
Tilled fields and ordered villages appeared before
the eyes of Charles' horsemen as they progressed.
With the new teachings, better conditions went

hand in hand. As the new pattern took form, the people were emerging from their animal-like forest ways to more nearly resemble their Frankish brothers in a rule of law.

Whatever skirmishes were encountered by the Frankish force came from those of the Alemanni, the Frisians, and the Saxons who clung to the old rule of tooth and claw. Charles exacted tribute and hostages from these people, not only to protect the peace of Frankland but to gain time for the development of more new settlements. There had been enough war and violence in Charles' life to make him understand that the successful war was the war which never got started. If Boniface could help in this, then he would support Boniface to the limit.

Secure, then, in their reputation for valor, the Franks plunged into the leafy undergrowth of the Saxon forests. Charles had already reminded his scouts and flankers of what they could expect.

"Whenever the Germans are alerted to the approach of a strong force entering their domain, they withdraw into the deepest parts of their forests. After they have learned of the nature and the errand of the invader, they make their plans and strike."

When the scouts had reported seeing nothing after three days of marching, the word was the same. Carelessness or acting on hasty assumption could mean a sudden and quiet death for a man who was farther away from his group than he should have been. Perhaps Charles had never heard the story of Varus, the Roman governor of Germany, who, hundreds of years before, had been lured into the German forests with three legions. All had been destroyed in three days of fighting; only the cavalry regained the banks of the Rhine. Yet, wise in the ways of the forest peoples, Charles never left anything to chance; the first mistake could be the last.

Sooner or later, Charles' command would arrive at a fortified place called a *werl* or *burg*. These defense points were also centers of trade and were set up as markets. The people themselves lived in the depths of the forest; they gathered in these places on market days or in times of war. Deeper in the forest the nobles lived on their estates. The *frilingi,* or freemen, were the warriors under the command of the *edhelingi,* or nobles; the *lazz* were "half free," that is, free to live their own lives but owing allegiance to a noble. The slaves were largely captives taken in raids.

"It is well to remember," Charles had told his younger followers, "that Frankland's safety lies in her unity. As long as the Frankish people remember that, there is no need to fear these people. As long as the German chieftains go on feuding among themselves, as long as they are dominated by their petty jealousies, they can never unite in any great undertaking."

And these same young leaders-in-training came to look on in wonder at seeing the power of their

The people lived in the depths of the forest.

leader's name bring the Germans from their forest hidings to render hostages and pay tribute.

Out of the burg came first a few wary figures, and Charles asked to speak to their noble or chief. Presently, on every side there were hundreds of faces peering out from among the trees. Charles, alert to the very fingertips, made it a point never to turn his head; such idle curiosity was beneath his notice. And Charles' young men looked to him to set the example in everything.

Once Charles had given proof of his power to the chieftain in a way that he could understand, the Frankish force withdrew with the hostages and the cattle which usually formed the tribute and moved on to the next point.

This was the nature of the situation confronting Boniface too. Without arms, without force of the kind understood by these Germans, he strengthened their Christian inclination. On the other hand, this was not to say that in years to come many of these tribes would not renounce Christianity and return to the old ways, through fear or threats by other tribes. Where people had been too hastily converted, there was always a danger of the new signs and symbols being used to cover the old pagan ones. Boniface blamed the Celtic monks for much of this and labored as vigorously in eliminating heresy as he did in baptizing new converts.

Two men in particular would later arouse the ire of Boniface in this regard, one Clement, a

Scot, and the other a Gaul named Adalbert who had been revered by the people and whose relics had been preserved by them. Adalbert had offended by erecting oratories and crosses near Druidical altars and religious sites which caused the people, in their confusion, to forsake their churches. Boniface had no patience with anyone who persisted in muddying the stream from which his people were to drink.

Charles, for his part, steadily widened the area of his influence by pushing eastward to the headwaters of the Danube and beyond. In intervening in the affairs of the Bavarian dukes, it became necessary to fight several battles, one near Regensburg, in order to make his position clear.

It was here that the missi reached Charles with the word that the Saracens had attacked Aquitaine for the second time by raiding Gascony!

"Have you no word from Odo himself?" Charles demanded testily. "Can I not turn my back for a moment without Odo's entire domus collapsing on his head?"

The bedraggled and weary messengers exchanged glances.

"Excellency, these reports come from your—er —representatives in Toulouse," one said. "The Duke of Aquitaine is with his troops, without doubt."

More messengers arrived. The Saracens, they said, had pushed north from their base at Narbonne, having overrun all of Septimania. After capturing Carcassone and Nîmes, they were moving up the Rhone Valley.

Charles began immediately to wind up his Bavarian campaign.

"Still no word from the Duke of Aquitaine, I see," Charles commented, as further reports arrived. "Perhaps it is just as well. He could be calling for help any time, and I had better be in a position to give it to him." His paladins grinned and nodded, commenting that it was usually difficult to predict what the Duke of Aquitaine would do.

This time, however, the Duke of Aquitaine seemed even more unpredictable than usual. Charles had fully expected Odo to go to the aid of the Burgundians in order to protect his own domain. In fact no one in Odo's position could possibly fail to take action. Yet not only was there no word from Odo, there seemed to be no word *about* him.

It was not until the Saracens had advanced to the city of Autun and sacked it that Charles really began to withdraw from his extended position. The Saône Valley was as a spear pointed at the heart of Frankland and the Saracens were holding that spear!

Suddenly, and for no reason that anyone could see at first, the Saracens gave up their campaign in Burgundy and returned to Narbonne!

Later, the cause of this change was learned. A struggle between two groups within the Saracen ranks had broken out, a struggle for leadership between the Ma'ddites and the Yemenites. The Saracen thrust of 725 had simply collapsed because of internal dissension.

Charles' feeling of relief that the problem of Saracens had solved itself for the moment was somewhat marred by his preoccupation with Odo's silence. Without his having to lift a finger, the victory had been delivered into Odo's hands! Yet Odo had made no move at any time; it almost looked as if he had known what was going to happen!

In Metz, Charles suddenly learned that his suspicions were justified. He had not heard from Duke Odo of Aquitaine because Odo had entered into an alliance with the Saracens!

The agent, newly arrived from Toulouse, delivered his message to his thunderstruck master. The man had ridden at top speed up the Roman road that runs along the banks of the Saône and then directly to Metz, and his exhaustion showed in his stance. The room had been cleared so that they could be alone, and Charles waved the messenger into a chair.

"This must have happened some time ago," protested Charles, angrily. "Why was I not told?"

"The matter was well hid, Excellency," was the reply. "Not many of Duke Odo's own people were aware of it. In the confusion of the Saracen struggle for power—"

Charles scowled.

Hurriedly, the messenger went on:

"It was in order to protect his southern borders, Excellency, that the Duke Odo entered into negotiations with the Saracen leader at Narbonne, a man by the name of Othman ben-abi-Nissa, as your Excellency well knows." He stammered, as he saw the hardening of Charles' scowl.

"Tell me about abi-Nissa. I have been told that he is one of the leaders of the Ma'ddite party. Also, that he is a man of ambition as well as power."

"This is quite true, Excellency. This man has even greater plans. The—er—differences which have arisen between the Ma'ddites and the Yemenites seem to be coming to a head. The issue is over the rule of Spain, no less."

Charles was silent for a long time.

"I see. Abi-Nissa plans to rule Spain at the head of the Ma'ddite party," he said. "Odo is backing him in his plans. Once abi-Nissa is ruler of all Moorish Spain with Odo as his ally, then *let the Frankish nation beware*. Is that it?"

This time it was the messenger's turn to remain silent.

Charles now called in his paladins to hear for themselves what the Duke of Aquitaine had done. The ring of Frankish faces showed first amazement and then anger. Exclamations broke out, threats and expressions of disbelief.

"I see that you feel as I do," remarked Charles, dryly. His own rage was gone now; already he was making his plans. "Let me first see to this man's needs." He flung the agent a bag of gold to be used in his business. His instructions were to return to Toulouse directly after he had eaten and rested. As the man left the room, Charles turned to his paladins and said:

"What you have just heard is either a monstrous fable or the mumbling in the beard of an old man in his dotage. Yet we cannot afford to disbelieve it. Within a day or so there will be other messengers who will either deny this whole story as being a base rumor or say that it is no rumor and offer some proof of its truth.

"I suggest we wait for further reports."

Charles had been away so much and had been so active while at home that his family had become like figures from a long-remembered dream. He had almost entirely persuaded Rotruda of his innocence in connection with the death of Grimoald. The boys were growing up, too, with the passage of time, and Charles longed to be with them more.

Much as he loved both boys, it always puzzled him what to talk to them about. Carloman, the elder boy, was a dreamer who kept to himself much of the time, although he was intelligent and attentive. Yet it seemed to the father that Carloman had neither the drive nor the desire to succeed him as mayor of the palace or even as a warrior. As he had grown into young manhood, he had taken to his training in arms and horsemanship with fair skill and enthusiasm, but showed nothing as yet of the traits that later sealed his destiny.

Pepin, the younger boy, later to be known as the "Short," was eight years younger than his brother. He was a quiet boy who had eyes only for his father. Often, when Charles had considered himself alone or in private conversation with some envoy, he discovered the little fellow listening from some dark corner, his eyes fixed unblinkingly upon his father. And yet, no matter what his age, Pepin always kept his own counsel.

This boy would grow up to be the father of the great Charlemagne. The greatness of his own father was clearly beyond him, but at least he had a pattern to follow. Carloman, on the other hand, would one day lay down his rulership as Austrasian mayor of the palace and enter the monastery of Montecassino, following an inner pattern, perhaps known only to himself.

Again the paladins were assembled as more reports flowed in from Aquitaine. As before, feelings ran high, for the new reports confirmed Odo's pact with the Saracens.

"An alliance has definitely been signed between Odo of Aquitaine and the Saracen leader, abi-Nissa," the messenger reported, "and, to seal the covenant, Duke Odo has given the hand of his daughter, Lampagie, in marriage to abi-Nissa!"

CHAPTER SIX
The Strategy of Duke Charles

Upon two little islands in the Seine stood the capital of Neustria, a fortified place where a number of roads came together. The Romans had called it Lutetia Parisii, or the "Muddy Place of the Parisians"; later on, the city would be known to a vastly different world as Paris.

When the Huns were approaching, a nun had told the frightened people to remain on their little islands, that the attack would come to nothing. And so it had turned out. The humble nun became known forever after as St. Genevieve, the patron saint of Paris. In this year of 731, her bones rested in the Church of the Holy Apostles, a spot to be one day occupied by the Pantheon. Even at this time, Paris was a city of churches: in St. Martin's, Clovis had been baptized; at the city's gates stood the monastery of St. Vincent; and nearby was the Basilica of St. Denis.

On a hill near the islands stood the palace of the Roman governor Julian, who had been acclaimed emperor on this spot by his troops. He had gone forth from here at their head to rule Rome. And now in this same palace, somewhat dilapidated by now, Charles had set up his headquarters.

Ragenfrid, former mayor of the palace of Neustria, had just died. No sooner had the funeral ceremonies been concluded than Charles proceeded to annex Neustria.

King Clotaire IV, whom Charles had put upon the Austrasian throne, had died in 719. The following year, Chilpèric II, who had been rescued by Charles from the clutches of Odo, also died, and the throne of Neustria was occupied by Thierry IV, who ruled over both Neustria and Austrasia. For all practical purposes, then, the two countries had already been united.

All this was a matter of outward form. The real ruler of Frankland was Charles, mayor of the palace. This was understood by everyone.

In the council chamber were gathered the war lords of Frankland to hear the latest reports from the south. As the men filed over the mosaic pavement to take their places at the table, Charles stood watching them, a grim smile on his face.

Charles addressed them, reminding them of Odo's alliance with the Saracens, a bargain he had sealed by giving the hand of his daughter Lampagie to abi-Nissa in marriage. Charles' face maintained his smile, now touched with a kind of triumph; the paladins looked at him expectantly, although they were puzzled.

"It is not my purpose, nobles, to bore you with the tedious details of the internal quarrels of the Saracens. You have been kept informed of the struggles between the Ma'ddites and the Yemenites, with the rulership of all Spain as the prize."

He laughed and looked about him at the faces turned toward him, as if weighing the value of each man.

"You know that the Ma'ddites have lost. What do you reckon is the value of Duke Odo's alliance with that party now? What is the worth of abi-Nissa's seal at the bottom of that treaty, eh, gentlemen?"

The faces of the councilors broke into broad grins. There were soft whistles of incredulity. One man slapped his hand on the table and laughed, and a buzz of excited comment arose.

"And now this." Charles waited until the room had quieted down. "A new leader has arisen among the Saracens, Abd-ar-Rahman, present leader of the Yemenites and possible ruler of Spain. Under his command, an army is gathering on the upper reaches of the River Ebro. From all appearances, leudes, it begins to look as if Aquitaine faces invasion by the Saracens."

There was no sound in the room now when Charles paused.

"Anyone who makes any kind of a pact with

these people is a fool. Whatever Odo's regrets may be at this moment they are as nothing compared to what he is going to feel."

Again the council chamber hummed with talk. There was some head-shaking which Charles perceived immediately.

"There can be no doubt, my leudes, what our fate will be if Odo fails now." The councilors saw his eyes alight with that devil's fire which had possessed him many times upon the battlefield when the odds were long. "The forces of the Saracens, like the sands of the sea for numbers, will beat upon our ranks until all Frankland is overrun with them, as it happened in Spain."

Every eye was fixed upon the duke; each man sensed that the next pronouncement would shake the very foundations of Julian's old palace. The chamber rang with the silence.

"Slowly the forces of Abd-ar-Rahman are gathering, secure in the knowledge that Odo will not attack them before they are ready to strike. To do that, Odo would need the help of the Franks." Charles laughed again and again, and his eyes lighted up. "We must, therefore, tempt Rahman before he is fully ready to attack Odo, before he has assembled all his men and resources. Once he is deep in Aquitaine, he will be closer to the Franks and farther from his bases in Spain."

The men nodded. The meaning of what Charles was saying began to take form in their minds.

"Nobles, we will call upon our allies from

across the Rhine, we will assemble every man we have, in preparation." Charles was crouching over the table now and he leveled his glance at each man as if he were sighting a weapon. "In the meantime, however, we go to invade Aquitaine from the north." He straightened up.

Milon, companion-in-arms of Charles from the earliest days, a man upon whom the duke had bestowed two bishoprics, spoke now. He alone could ask the question which had entered the mind of every man there. No one else made a sound.

"Excellency, we have followed you through the campaigns from Amblève to Regensburg, and there was no murmur from your paladins; no soldier ever complained. Now you propose to attack Aquitaine with whom we must continue to be allies in the event that the Saracens invade Gaul.

"You have only to give the command, Excellency," he hastened to add, "and we will follow you against all the demons of the earth. Yet, tell us, as we are your brothers-in-arms, are we to lift the mace against Odo, as well as against the Saracens?"

Charles smiled as if he had hoped this question would be raised. With deep satisfaction he explained that a quick thrust, say, at Bourges, deep in Aquitanian territory, would convince Abd-ar-Rahman that Odo was in trouble with his Frankish neighbors to the north. What would it take, after all? A lightning dash across the Loire and an investment of the city until such time as the news of the venture reached the ears of the Saracen commander. Then—to retire quickly. No lives lost; no villages burnt; no cities destroyed; the invasion of Aquitaine would turn the trick alone! If necessary, the thrust could be repeated.

If any voice had been raised to ask the question, "But what of Odo?" the owner of that voice would have been laughed to scorn. Odo had betrayed them to the Saracens, hadn't he? Then how did Odo merit further consideration? He and Rahman alike would be reckoned merely pawns on the Frankish chessboard of strategy.

Once more the Frankish forces were on the move. Spring of 732 saw Charles' troops crossing the Loire at heavy flood in skiffs and rafts. The most direct route was selected, and the columns hurried southward.

Charles made no secret of his invasion of Aquitaine; as his spearmen advanced in swift stages across the country, he even helped to spread the alarm by adding threats to his warlike gestures. The walls of Bourges were quickly encircled; the terrified and puzzled citizens, hastily armed, looked down on the Frankish forces from the Roman towers. Charles had no war machines such as the Romans had; he contented himself with cutting off all access to the city from the Cher River and the neighboring villages. And then he waited.

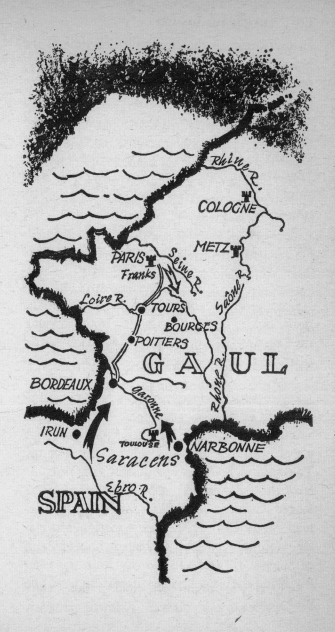

Envoys from Odo appeared to find out the meaning of the unprovoked assault. Later, Odo himself rode onto the scene. What was the meaning of this siege of Bourges? To all who inquired, Charles calmly explained that Duke Odo's pact with the Saracens, now gathering on the Spanish frontier, was an act of war against the Franks. As a matter of fact, by signing this treaty, Odo had nullified the peace of 720, signed between Aquitaine and Frankland!

Odo rode off with his optimates and began issuing orders immediately for his troops to take action against Charles. In doing this, he left only a token force to watch the Saracens. When the attention of Odo was thus completely divided, two things happened almost at once.

Abd-ar-Rahman issued from the valley of the Ebro and crossed into Aquitaine from Irun. As a part of this movement, the Saracens at Narbonne moved north and west to join Rahman's forces somewhere near Bordeaux.

The second event took place when Charles abandoned his siege of Bourges and retired across the Loire!

"Now that the Saracen has taken the bait," said Charles, amiably, "let Odo find out for us how strong he is. In this way we shall learn how many of our allies to call in to defeat the renowned Saracen."

Summer wore on and the conflagration in the south spread. As disaster followed disaster,

Charles assembled his Franks and his German allies. Paris was the point of concentration; in the growing threat, it had become for the time the new capital of Frankland.

Rahman moved up the sea coast and drove for Bordeaux. It was there that Odo planned to meet him. There were still enough fortifications left from Roman days to cause Odo to believe that the city would be a good place to make a stand. Since the Garonne River served to cut off possible retreat, the Duke of Aquitaine felt secure in his position, with the bulk of his forces massed between the Dordogne and the Garonne, holding open the crossing and using Bordeaux as his right-wing anchor position.

Odo was about sixty-three years old at this time. Perhaps he had become careless. Perhaps he underestimated the skill of the Saracen. At any rate, he was evidently not expecting an enemy force to come at him from the east. By the time the duke and his commanders knew what was happening, the Aquitanian forces had been crushed between the two rivers and cut to ribbons. Bordeaux was next found to be less than impregnable; the Saracen warriors, greedy for loot, swarmed through the breached walls to plunder, massacre, and burn.

As the fleeing remnants of Odo's army, as well as terrified surviving citizens, fled northward, crossing the rivers by any means they could, Odo decided to go for help. As he raced northward with his fideles, the pillars of smoke of the burning city formed a vast pall behind him, a black curtain of apparent doom. What was happening to Bordeaux would soon be the fate of all Aquitanian cities. Toulouse was lost to view for the moment; Arles was also burning. The pattern of the Saracen was well known, "massacre, pillage, and burn." It never seemed to vary.

The Saracens concluded their orgy of pillaging, left the valley of the Garonne, and moved northward across the Dordogne, sluggish with victory and spoil. They had learned that in the holy city of Tours vast treasure had been accumulated through the years and stored at the Church of St. Martin. As they swarmed out over the countryside in several columns, they had almost lost sight of their objectives in their lust for booty.

Afterward Arab scribes would write of Abd-ar-Rahman in these words:

"And Abd-ar-Rahman and other prudent cavaliers saw the disorder of the Moslem troops who were loaded with spoil; but they did not venture to displease the soldiers by ordering them to abandon everything except their arms and their horses. And Abd-ar-Rahman trusted in the valor of his soldiers, and in the good fortune which had ever attended him."

The Arabs may not have had any misgivings, but what was the terror of the Aquitanians themselves at seeing their country overwhelmed by these locusts? The monks later wrote their own chronicles of these times:

"There issued from Spain the Saracens and their king who was called Abd-ar-Rahman, and their wives and their children and all their belongings in such great multitudes that no one could reckon or number them. They brought with them all their armor and whatever else they had as if they were thenceforth always to dwell in Gaul."

As the weeks passed, the Moslem horsemen "rode at their will through all the land of the Narbonne, Toulouse, and Bordeaux," with no one to dispute their ravages and destruction. Not only were the Saracens an army of cavalry; they had brought thousands of mules to carry away booty, as well as to carry their tents and equipment. There were no wagons or carts; food was obtained by foraging.

The Roman road from Bordeaux to Poitiers was overrun with the invaders for mile after mile; they not only encountered no resistance but they traveled the best of roads! Odo's domain, for all practical purposes, was lost.

The Aquitanians rode into Paris and made their way to the palace through streets choked with fighting men. Duke Odo and his fideles as well, exhausted with fighting and riding, for the first time began to take heart. Surely Charles was aware of the danger of the Saracens, not only to Aquitaine but to Frankland also. The man who once had referred with contempt to the "half-naked German chieftains" was now very happy indeed to see so many of them on hand!

Hunald spoke:

"There is a different spirit at work here, my father. Here one feels the gathering of the forces as before a great storm; here is the feeling of power and hope, as the great Charles forges his new weapons."

Even though his son had expressed Odo's own feelings quite accurately, the duke's weariness caused him to burst out irritably:

"No matter what goes awry in the world, there is always the 'great Charles!' My faith! What would we do without the 'great Charles' to come to our aid?"

Quickly he fell silent and looked away. Hunald, whose admiration of Charles was undisguised, was aware of his father's jealousy of the "great Charles" and smiled wryly. Odo's irritation would hardly help matters when the time came for the discussion of their situation. Hunald could only hope for the best.

The party entered the portals of Julian's old palace through the throngs of officials and courtiers. Odo afterward remarked that he had felt they were "poor relatives" coming to beg, although Hunald pointed out that a number of the officials had stepped aside as soon as they recognized the Aquitanian emblems. It was sundown; servants were lighting torches in the corridors, and from the kitchens came odors that told of preparations for a meal. If only he weren't so desperately tired, Odo reflected bitterly. The entire summer had been spent in fighting a white-garbed enemy who seemed to multiply at each sword stroke. They rose up in waves out of the earth itself, to battle more fiercely with every step. Behind them rose huge columns of smoke as the cities and fields were laid waste.

And now there was this ride for help, a ride of hundreds of leagues in long stages to visit a man who had always shown himself to be more of an enemy than a friend. Which would he be now?

Odo looked up from the black welter of these thoughts to find that they were already in the council chamber in the presence of this very same "great Charles." Hunald was speaking; all others were listening courteously for the most part, although there were some pitying smiles.

"—that I might remind Your Excellency that my father, having ridden hard, is rather tired—"

Odo looked down at his torn and mud-splattered garments, and closed his eyes to hide the quick tears of helpless rage. Tired, indeed! Why, when he was the age of that young man, he could. . . . He shook his head with the futility of his thoughts. It were far better that a fighting man die in battle in the flower of his youth than to live to be an old man, as he was now. Far better.

"I shall speak for myself!" he told the assemblage proudly. He nodded toward his son. "If I must in all truth own that I am a little weary in body, I can say with equal truth that no one can find fault or flaw in my spirit."

If anyone had been watching Charles at that moment, he might have seen a glimmer of admiration in his eyes; Odo was a man, for all his losses.

"I am here, sir, to ask for help. I cannot say that I deserve it through either my skill as a soldier or because of my wisdom in the selection of my friends. You may laugh, gentlemen, if you choose. Whatever I have done is past now. It is the present and the future which must be dealt with, and I am ready to play my part in it whether for victory against the Saracen or for an honorable death."

Odo was asking no quarter. There were no sneers now, nothing to indicate anything less than respect. Successful in war as Charles' paladins had been, they were all aware that not one of their number had ever met the Saracen in battle. Odo and Hunald had. The Moors were a new enemy; the reports of their prowess grew with every passing day. One report which persisted and grew was of their numbers. Seemingly, the Saracens multiplied like insects.

"Tell me, sir," Charles said, "is it true that when you signed the pact you gave your daughter's hand in marriage to abi-Nissa? I find this hard to believe."

The mere mention of his daughter brought the

"No one can find fault in my spirit."

old man to tears; up to this point he had been standing erect as in his proudest day. Now he had to be helped to a seat.

"I ask your pardon, sir," Hunald broke in, "but Lampagie was very dear to her father's heart—and to her brother's also." He paused: "However, the story is quickly told. Abi-Nissa and others joined with Musa-ibn-Nusair to overthrow the Yemenites and take over the rule of Spain. Twenty years before, Musa had commanded all Moorish forces in their invasion of that country and his plans seemed sound and good. However, Abd-ar-Rahman rallied the Yemenites and utterly routed the rebels. Musa was killed; it was said that abi-Nissa escaped torture by leaping to his death from a cliff in the Pyrenees—and it may be true. The Ma'ddites were destroyed as a party—and, of course, my father's alliance died with them at the same time."

The only sound was the guttering of the torches in the room.

"And your sister, Lampagie?"

Hunald lowered his head quickly.

"My sister became part of the spoils of war. Word of her has reached us from time to time in strange ways." He sighed. "The last we heard of her was that she had been taken to Damascus and there sold as a slave. By now, no doubt, she belongs to some fat caliph or trader—who knows?"

Charles had brought up this subject deliberately. He had heard such rumors, of course, but he had to make sure of Odo. The erratic behavior of the man in the past warranted, in his mind, the need to secure his total commitment to the coming campaign by whatever means were available. Who could say what new alliance Odo would sign if he thought it might be to his advantage? Therefore, if Odo had a personal reason for wanting the Saracens destroyed, in addition to that of the loss of his realm, so much the better. The Frank never did things by halves!

Charles gave orders that the Aquitanians were to be given comfortable quarters and an opportunity to rest, while in the following days he continued his preparations for war.

There were later meetings between Odo and Charles; plans were quickly set up for reorganizing the defeated Aquitanian armies on Frankish soil. There were food and weapons for all Aquitanians who could cross the Loire to join their duke.

"To the Duke of Aquitaine may I say that I shall be pleased to have him as an ally," Charles said. The chamber was filled with attentive Franks and the men of Aquitaine. "Our understanding is that the supreme command of our forces shall be in the hands of the Franks. This is as it should be and I know we are in agreement." He paused as if waiting to hear if any objections would be raised. Odo dropped his gaze; all were silent.

"Then there remains only that all present, by

their oath sworn before me on their knees, shall resolve never to turn aside from the swift defeat of the Saracens until victory or our death shall be accomplished." Charles drew his sword and all followed suit. When the oath had been duly sworn, the Duke of Aquitaine stood up.

"In this hour of our country's trial, we of Aquitaine cheerfully swear this oath, acknowledging our mistakes in the past and joining now with our Frankish neighbors as allies, without reservations. However," and now Odo stood as tall and proud as ever he had in the past, "let it be known that we, too, are men of warlike tradition and skill, having tested Moslem valor in countless past engagements. We are eager to meet the Saracen again, for unlike the Franks, we fight to avenge the loss of our families, our ravaged fields, and our looted cities."

Having said his little piece in a bid, perhaps, to secure some measure of respect for his own defeated troops, Duke Odo strode from the chamber. Charles caught the eye of Hunald and something very like a twinkle passed between them. Charles then murmured under his breath a few words which Hunald could not catch. Instead the Aquitanian read the expression of the Frank, and if it could have been put into words, the words would have been:

"This is what I have been waiting to hear. . . ."

CHAPTER SEVEN

The Battle for Tours

"If you follow my advice you will not interrupt their march nor precipitate your attack. They are like a torrent which is dangerous to stem in its career. The thirst for riches and the consciousness of success redouble their valor, and valor is to more avail than arms or numbers. Be patient till they have loaded themselves with the encumbrances of wealth. The possession of wealth will divide their counsels and assure your victory."

With these words, quoted since in many chronicles, Charles counseled the Duke of Aquitaine, possibly at a time when both had come upon the first efforts of the Saracens to plunder Tours. Written down and passed on, the phrases reveal the insight and experience of the Frankish leader. Even if the words themselves are the work of some chronicler of later centuries, the character they show is confirmed by the man's deeds.

From a hillside overlooking the city, the two leaders watched the looting of Tours. Odo was livid; the fury of the man was greater because he was unable to take any action. Charles, on the other hand, was attentive but detached, as if he were merely watching a procession of white ants entering and leaving their hill.

"I have acknowledged your leadership"—Odo's voice shook like a taut bowstring—"and I will keep my oath. Were I alone, however, there would be a far different scene. At the head of my people, I would fall upon that rabble and thrust their booty down their swollen gullets! With these hands I would—" There were simply no words left to express his feelings; the old duke was pitiful in his helplessness.

Charles saw that there were few fires, actually; little damage had been done as yet. Apparently the present vandals were only some advanced units of the Saracens; the main body not yet arrived. Odo, on the other hand, had eyes only for the raiders as they straggled in and out of the city, loaded down with plunder. They were disorganized and strung out in a way that invited attack, but so fearful were the townspeople of Saracen vengeance that no one lifted a hand to stop them.

"The River Cher is their greatest hazard now," mused Charles. "They must know that every minute they spend in the city they are in a trap."

This was true. Tours lies on a level tongue of land between the Loire and the Cher rivers, a few miles east of the point where they join. The citizens of the town had destroyed the bridge over the Cher, which the Saracens had crudely repaired. The bridge could be easily destroyed again, and Franks moving on the city from the east could close the trap. Charles pointed across the Cher.

"If we can also bring our forces south of the city, the Saracens would have to withdraw. Well, we shall see whether their greed is greater than their concern for their own lives."

A part of the Frankish army had crossed the Loire at Orleans, whereas Charles and Odo had come down the valley by way of the Roman road which lies on the north bank of the river. Their followers were strung out behind them for several miles while the two leaders reconnoitered. However, before Charles could give any orders, the movements of the Saracens underwent a sudden change. As one man, the raiders were streaming from the city almost as if they had overheard Charles' words! To Charles, however, it was obvious that the Saracens had received news of his approach.

"We will give them a little time to get under way and then enter the city to see what damage has been done." He gave orders for his troops to cross the Cher and await further orders when they reached the banks of the Indre.

As Charles' troops began to move, the Saracen withdrawal became general. Word reached the two leaders that the whole Moslem host was falling back, possibly to find a suitable place for a meeting, one less cut up, perhaps, by brooks and streams. In addition, while the Saracens had attacked Poitiers and set fire to the Basilica of St. Hilary, they had sealed off the town and hurried on to Tours. Some of the defenders might just possibly be holding out.

Meanwhile, Charles and Odo rode into Tours. They made their way through the rubble and confusion, to the Basilica of St. Martin, where the bulk of treasure had been stored. Marks on the wall showed where the Saracens had tried to set fire to the buildings, but these attempts had been quickly extinguished by the townspeople as the Arabs fled the city. Moreover, there was still treasure there, overlooked by the fugitives.

Upon this spot, St. Martin, the "Apostle of the Gauls" and first Bishop of Tours, had been buried. Over the tomb, the first basilica had been built in 472. A hundred years later, Gregory of Tours, bishop, and first historian of France, restored it. He modeled his building upon the Church of the Holy Sepulchre at Jerusalem, with the saint's tomb in the center of a large rotunda.

St. Martin had started life as a Roman soldier, had become a hermit, then a bishop, and was later canonized as a saint. It was he who had established the monasteries of Gaul. Since the death of St. Martin, Tours had been a holy city; to this spot had come the pilgrims, among them Gregory, who, as a young man, had first arrived to seek a cure for a serious illness. Here, too, the gifts and tithes had accumulated over the years until the reputation of its wealth had made St. Martin's famous.

This was the reason why the Saracen host had directed their march to St. Martin's Church in Tours. This was the place where Frankish and Aquitanian arms would meet their supreme test. Not only the treasure, but a newly forming civilization was at stake.

For several days, levies from the north streamed in. Men from the Black Forest and the swamps of the North Sea lands jostled the levies of Neustria and Austrasia; among the latter was Hugh, grandson of Plectrude and nephew of Charles, barely in his twenties at this time. Hugh had been only a child when Pepin died, and so Plectrude had ruled Austrasia as regent in young Hugh's place as mayor of the palace. If Charles still needed a hostage to protect himself against Plectrude, he had it in Hugh, yet there was no bitterness in the young man toward his uncle for having taken over his office. On the contrary, Hugh was eager to make a name for himself under his famous uncle.

The Frankish armies and their allies pushed slowly on up the valley of the Clain until they were in sight of the junction of the Vienne. Here a kind of plain stretched southwestward in the direction of Poitiers; the ruins of Cenon were still smoking. Some contact with the enemy was made during this time but seemingly the actions were slight, merely testing the mettle of the enemy from both sides. Almost without orders, the Frankish troops spread out in a rough battle line, cutting off the road that led to Tours.

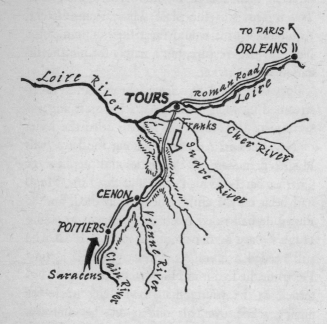

The Saracens, containing the city of Poitiers some dozen miles away, were forming for their own part, and the smoke of the cooking fires of their camp gave the illusion that another city had sprung up overnight. Charles' scouts were much impressed by the spirit and numbers of the Saracen horses. Whereas the Frankish army was an army of infantry with comparatively few horses, the Arabs were an army of cavalry with every man a skilled horseman. Seemingly, their troops were made up of all the nations through which they had passed, and the number of languages spoken gave them the name of "Europenses," or "men speaking many tongues." In addition, there were renegades of the Mediterranean—Greeks, Tartars, Syrians, even Persians—who had come along in hope of plunder, rascals who had no interest in the advancement of Islam or any other faith. From North Africa had come Berber cavalry who showed off their skill by incessant feats of horsemanship as they rode up and down the lines.

Seven days passed; foraging parties from both armies encountered each other constantly. Savage little battles broke out, and many an Arab was toppled from his steed by an ax thrown from the skilled hand of a Frank; a Moor could show his skill with the scimitar, too, as he whirled past on a galloping stallion. Most of the Arabs rode according to their family groups; they mourned their fallen relatives and then sought vengeance upon the first Frankish soldiers they encountered. Larger and larger groups of warriors of both armies met; a brisk exchange would follow, then a quick breakaway and retreat. Thus the armies cautiously tested each other for seven days; for seven days they took each other's measure.

In reconnoitering the Saracen situation from the hills across the Clain River, it may have been possible for Charles to witness the great phenomenon of Islam, along with troop movements and military matters. He may have watched the muezzins calling the faithful to prayer, as it was carried out five times a day. To see a whole army on its knees facing eastward to the holy city of Mecca was a sight never to be forgotten by any witness, as the invaders touched their foreheads to the earth.

Most certainly the arms of the Christian warriors had been blessed by their bishops on the field. Perhaps Charles himself, with Odo and others of his leaders, had knelt at the tomb of St. Martin before hurrying on to the scene of preparation for battle. St. Martin was a soldier's saint; he and Charles might have had much in common had they lived in the same period. Perhaps Charles had heard the story of how St. Martin, as a young Roman legionnaire, had seen a beggar huddled at a city gate shivering with cold. Martin, it was said, stepped from the ranks and cut in half the heavy red soldier's cloak he wore and flung the piece over the beggar's shoulders. That night he had a dream and in the dream, behold, there stood Christ, wearing the halved cloak!

It was a tender tale taken to the hearts of a people who, though often cruel themselves, could be touched by such a story.

In the war councils, Odo put forth his position. He did not ask or beg to be recognized as the commander of all Aquitanian armies in the field; he stated his position clearly so that Charles, his paladins, and the remaining Frankish commanders on down to young Hugh would understand it. Aquitanian arms had suffered grievous defeat; it was Odo's intention that the German leaders would understand, in spite of this, that the Aquitanians were the men of experience in the present situation.

"Perhaps it is best that we speak frankly of these things now." Charles' voice, as well as his gaze, was level. "The Saracen is not a man to be dismayed by stories of Frankish arms; perhaps he has never heard such stories. That he will hurl his full might against us when the time comes is not to be doubted. How then are we to withstand the enemy if we are not all of one mind, of one command?"

Odo was silent for a moment. Behind him was a long trail of mistakes—the results of misplaced confidence and judgment. Yet at times he had shown brilliance as a military commander. If only his jealousy of Charles could be curbed somehow.

"Make no mistake, sir. I have given my oath as I have said before. You are supreme commander here; that we will all acknowledge. Yet as the German troops will fight under their own leaders, as the Frankish levies will fight under their counts and dukes, just so will the Aquitanians redeem their country from the Saracen under the command of their duke." Odo's voice was strong and firm.

"These men have suffered greatly, nobles, they have suffered not only by the wounds in their bodies but in their minds and hearts also. They have lost wives and families; they have seen their cities and villages destroyed and their fields ravaged. Yet, more than this, to soldiers honor is precious, and this they feel they have lost. There is not one of them who is not happy and eager to attack, not one unwilling to give his life to drive out the invader. If we go to our death in this, then I will go at their head. In a like manner, if it be God's will, I will lead them to victory!"

These words lighted the faces of the Germans; these were sentiments they could understand. Charles saw this at once and the sarcastic remark he had been tempted to make remained unuttered.

"What assurance do you want of me?" he asked, warily.

"That we fight under our own banners and our own leaders for our own countries."

Charles' one great fear had been that at some point in the coming attack, at a time when complete unity was most important to all of the troops, Odo would go off on some notion of his own. Odo's name, in Charles' mind, had always been associated with all that was unreliable and unstable; at Amblève, Duke Odo had shown himself to be treacherous. Charles had lived with this idea for many years and it was not one easily thrown off.

The meeting was ended suddenly by the entrance of two of the mounted scouts who had been keeping the Saracen host under observation. Charles told Odo that he would give his answer in the morning after he had had time to consider the reports of the scouts.

The men reported that great activity was apparent in the Saracen camp; bonfires were burning and the holy men seemed to be haranguing the soldiers, inciting them to action. Judging by the preparations being made, the attack would come soon. Perhaps tomorrow would be the day, perhaps sooner.

Charles questioned the men and then sent them on their way. Other reports came in confirming the observations of the first two. Quietly the troops were awakened and put on a stand-to alert. Rain started to fall, putting a chill into the darkness of this October night as well as dampening the watch fires. The men were silent for the most part but there was no sense of panic or anxiety. The feeling seemed to be that this was the moment they had been waiting for; tomorrow would answer many questions. The rain ceased; some of the men lay down on the ground to doze fitfully while others watched. Far down the line, a minstrel was singing a ballad and his listeners were joining in from time to time. This was a sound which set many another man to dreaming.

It was a lonely, longing kind of song with a droop and quaver after each phrase.

The encounters with the Saracens during the week had taught the men of the north that new lances were needed, lances that were longer and heavier in the shaft. If a man tried to stop a galloping horse with a light lance it was sure to shatter and send him spinning. The trick was to hold the lance with the point raised at an angle from the ground, with the foot on the butt end to steady it. In this way the impact would be borne by the earth itself. Now as quickly as they were brought up, the new lances were distributed to all those who had not yet been supplied. There were few bows and arrows; the skillful archers of the future were a generation away for the Franks, but the Saracens had a few units of bowmen.

The first pale rays of the dawn crossed the sky; far to the east, rain clouds were spilling their contents on the distant hills while, overhead, patches of blue were spreading. A slight mist hung over the river on the left. There lay the men of Aquitaine.

"I am here for my answer." Odo's voice broke into Charles' reflections at this early hour like a discordant note. "The men of Aquitaine are looking to me to lead them. What am I to tell them?"

Charles had come to no decision on this. If only Hunald, Odo's son, were in command! The younger man was so much easier to work with and it was obvious that he sought to learn all he could from his Frankish ally.

"Tell them," Charles said quietly, "what you told us all last night in council. Tell them every word; and Hunald will ride with you to attest the valor of his noble father." Again he managed to catch Hunald's eye; the younger man nodded slightly and the Aquitanians left.

In this way, by establishing a relationship with the son, Charles sought to establish some sort of control over the father. If Odo should forget his pledges now, Hunald would be at his elbow to remind him. Only a fool took chances that could be avoided.

There was a sound now like distant thunder. It was low and muttering but it did not die away. Instead, it gathered in volume; it became a steady drumming which caught and held the attention of every man in the Frankish forces. Up the river toward Poitiers, past the ruins of Cenon, appeared what looked at first like a white ground mist which crept toward them over the plain. Exclamations of wonder broke out among the Franks as they realized what it was they were seeing.

Horsemen in flowing robes! Thousands of them. Horsemen! They were spread out across the plains as far as the eye could see. Sunlight gleamed in patches on the Damascus blades; flashes of light bounded from the points of the lances. Overhead flew the war standards in all colors, and as the enemy drew closer the battle cries could be heard even over the thunder of the horses' hoofs.

How slowly they seemed to move! The enemy was a white form writhing over the ground, but the lances resembled leaves of grass that reared out of a snowbank.

There was no sound now in Frankish ranks. Each man was watching this exhibition almost as if he were in some kind of trance.

"Stand close, men of Frankland!" came the order. "Stand close and make the Saracens know that they have encountered the wall that will permit them to go no further."

Behind the first ranks more men came running up; another wave and another, carrying the new big lances. Now the Franks were ten men deep, packed solidly together almost shoulder to shoulder. More men ran up to back them up.

"Stand close! Stand close!" rang the order. The paladins rode up and down making sure that these commands were being carried out in order and with understanding. "Bucklers high! Hold them high, you men of the north! Let them overlap if you can."

Someone in the rear started a battle song, and in a few seconds a thousand throats were swelling with the chorus. There were no tactics; there were few orders and most of them had already been given. Spirit was the thing now; let the battle chants be sounded, and the joy of combat would overflow every heart.

In the German ranks the same thing was taking place; to them this was the proper business of a man, to die in glorious battle and be remembered with honor, or to taste glorious victory. These men were Christians now, but behind their Christianity flowed the forces of Wotan and Thor. Overhead screamed the Valkyrie, urging them on to deeds of heroism and renown; there was no fear in these ranks—Valhalla itself was literally only a few furlongs away. . . .

The Saracens were closer; the dark faces bronzed by the rays of many a desert sun contrasted with the white cloud of their mantles; Paradise was for each who fell that day, or victory for those who survived. Defeat was not possible in either case.

So far they had ridden at a fast trot; now the men urged their mounts to a full gallop, and the lances were lowered almost like a portcullis being let down. The thunder of the hoofs filled the air; it was a steady roar and still growing. Many a Frank standing braced against the impact that was so soon to come could feel the trembling of the earth under his feet.

As the charge neared the point of contact, a few franciscas spun through the air, dropping some of the riders from the saddle; now the spear points were lowered in the Frankish masses, the butts were pounded into the earth, the ranks closed up.

The shock of impact was the climax in a vast ocean of sound. As the horses went down row upon row, the men in the rear ranks of the Franks climbed over the bodies of their own dead and wounded to come to grips with the unhorsed Arabs struggling on the ground. Some of the injured horses rose up and fell backward on their riders; more Saracens, not being able to rein in in time, were thrown over their horses' heads. The air sang as the throwing axes emptied more saddles; riderless mounts galloped wildly across the field, getting in the way of other horsemen coming to the attack.

Now the Franks drew their swords and moved forward. Most of the dismounted Arabs had lost their lances but drew their scimitars to give battle on foot. They had no body armor but neither did the Frankish foot-soldiers. In the melee that began shaping up, the Saracen attack had lost its power. The Franks pressing forward from the rear quickly finished off the Arabs who had been dismounted by the lances.

When the Franks next looked up from their grim work, they found that the attack had been broken. Moorish horsemen were drawing back, leaving their wounded behind.

No one, however, in either army made the mistake of thinking that the battle was over; even as the attackers withdrew, more Saracens were massing behind them to attack. Their emirs rode up and down uttering their harsh cries of command and exhortation.

All at once a kind of quiet came over the Saracen hordes. As the rearing and plunging horses were quieted and the men themselves straightened their lines, the Franks, Germans, and men of Aquitaine saw a magnificent sight. A small but colorful body of horsemen was riding in front of the Saracen line. Now a real hush fell upon the Arab host; all eyes of both armies were upon the riders inspecting the Arab ranks.

It was Abd-ar-Rahman, leader of the Yemenite party, master of Spain, and supreme commander of all Saracen forces in Gaul.

CHAPTER EIGHT

The Treasure of St. Martin's

"Stand to!" The voices of the counts and paladins were hoarse. "Stand to! Close up, there, close up!"

Murmurs ran down the line like wildfire:

"They are coming. They are going to try again."

The pounding of the horses' hoofs became a roar; it was thunder that was bearable only because it was unbelievable. Surely in all this world, there was never a sound so calculated to strike terror to the heart of a man, to put a kind of haze of unreality over everything, to numb every normal feeling. The pikes were lifted again; more reserves closed in from behind to brace for the shock of the Saracen charge.

The warriors in white now let go the reins of their horses; they would need to have their hands free to handle the shields and scimitars. The mounts thus freed sprang forward as if they had been shot from catapults. They were guided only by the pressure of the riders' knees against their flanks.

When the plunging animals encountered the pikes of the Franks, the shock was felt even by the reserves not directly engaged. Again the Saracens' horses went down; horses behind them hurtled over them, their riders thrown high in the air. Punctuating the cries of men and horses were the sharp cracks of splintering lances. Again the rear echelons of the Franks waded through the struggling masses of wounded, cutting and slashing whenever a Saracen raised his head.

Again the enemy was beaten off. Again they charged—and again, and again.

There came a time, at last, when the enemy had to draw off to rest. Yet at the same time, fresh units were being brought up and formed. Once more the flashing robes of Abd-ar-Rahman and his staff appeared as the leaders encouraged their men.

While the Franks watched these preparations for renewed combat, Duke Odo rode toward Charles. Behind him, Hunald and the staff followed. Some of them had been wounded but all were jubilant. In all the fury of the wild charges the Christian line had held!

As Odo drew rein at some distance from Charles, Hunald rode forward to make a request on his father's behalf.

"Well, young man," Charles said affably, "I was wondering when you and your father, the duke, would come forward with a plan that would save us from the Saracen."

The patronizing air was a little too much for Hunald; he flushed but tried to smile. After all, the Aquitanians had given a good account of themselves.

"It is my father's thought," Hunald began, "that the Aquitanians might be more useful if, during the next attack, they could threaten the Saracen rear. He has remembered your words of counsel and agrees that the Moor might like nothing better than to make away with his booty."

Charles leaned forward in the saddle. "I am listening," he said.

Hunald shot a troubled look as his father sitting stiff and straight in the saddle in the midst of his staff. Charles had suspected that Odo would want to make some independent move and now here it was. Hunald was his father's envoy; no doubt the old duke could not trust himself to ask the favor he wanted.

"If a blow could be struck at the Saracen camp," Hunald quickly pointed out, "my father, the duke, feels that the enemy might lose his resolve through fear for his plunder." He paused.

The point was well taken; Charles saw that such a move would serve to break the fury of the

Saracen thrusts. It would give the old man the chance to regain his honor at the same time.

"Let us speak with your father, the duke," snapped Charles. The two rode up to where Odo was waiting. In the consultation that followed, personal animosities were laid aside, insofar as this was possible, but almost before the war council had ended, Aquitanian horsemen were pulled back and light infantry units followed. These men would cross the Clain and circle to the south.

An hour passed.

The waiting was almost as hard to bear as the fighting itself. Charles brought up all his reserves to fill the gap left by the men of Aquitaine. The next attack would have all the might of the Saracen behind it; the wall of Franks braced for the storm.

They came, a great white sea flowing swiftly over the plain. This time, however, Abd-ar-Rahman and his champions were leading the way. The battle flags glowed in the light of the sinking sun; to many men in the Frankish ranks there was a haze of blood over everything. For many of them this was the last scene they would ever see, yet, as one man, they stood quietly, waiting. . . .

This time, as the horses went down and the spinning axes filled the air, the follow-up waves of Saracens began to dismount, to advance on foot. The Franks for their part surged forward, the battle cries swelling their throats. As the men of both armies stood thigh to thigh, the weapons rose and fell like sickles in a wheat field. The lines rolled forward and back. At such a time it is impossible to gauge the passage of the hours or tell how long such an action is going on. Dimly, at first, the men on both sides became aware that the light was failing. Dusk had somehow come upon them, yet everyone fought on as if he knew at this moment all that was at stake.

There was a sudden outcry in the Saracen ranks, a number of the warriors fought free and mounted their horses. Those already mounted were turning and leaving the battle. The emirs screamed at them, struck at them with their swords and, when this did no good, mounted and rode off themselves. Rahman, seeing this, tried in his turn to rally his forces, and the Franks pushed forward. Charles himself tried to force his way to the enemy commander, but was turned aside by riderless horses stampeding from the scene over the bodies of the fallen.

A ring of Franks were pressing toward Abd-ar-Rahman and his richly dressed officers. By this time, the Saracen commander was fighting for his life; the battle itself was secondary.

The Arab's scribes would one day describe it this way:

"The men of the north stood as motionless as a wall; they were like a belt of ice frozen together and not to be dissolved as they slew the Arabs with the sword. The Austrasians, vast of limb and iron of hand, hewed on bravely in the thick of the fight; it was they who found and cut down the Saracen king."

Abd-ar-Rahman was dead, pierced through by many lances, and numbers of his companions-in-arms had died with him. The Moslems rallied briefly to form a wall around their chief and the other fallen officers; behind this, others worked feverishly to drag away the bodies, that they might not fall into infidel hands.

The Saracen army was now in full flight; many who had lost their mounts seized others which were galloping riderless across the field and made off.

It had all happened so quickly; one minute the battle had been raging at its height, now the Moslems were melting away on every side in seeming panic. Few understood what had happened; Frankish trumpets were sounding to keep the men from pursuing the enemy, for darkness had fallen over the field and it would be difficult to see.

"Stay where you are!" was the order now. "Let no man follow! Stay where you are!"

In a short time the only Saracens to be seen were those huddled on the ground under their crumpled cloaks, some groaning from pain, most lying very still. Charles' horsemen reported that the enemy was retreating to Poitiers, where the Saracen camp stood overlooking the river. The

Moslems guarding the camp reported to those returning from battle that the camp had been attacked by a fairly small number of "men of the north," who had swum their horses across the stream, but that they had speedily beaten them off. The plunder, for all practical purposes, was safe, but two things had happened. The Saracen warriors had left the scene of an important battle out of personal concern for their booty; and, second, they had lost their leader. The full meaning of this was not apparent until later when riders from Spain reached them with the news that the Berbers in Maghreb, in northern Africa, had risen in revolt. Too hastily converted to Islam, they had struck when Abd-ar-Rahman was busy in Aquitaine.

All this was known to Charles some time later, of course, but at this moment he was welcoming back the Duke of Aquitaine and his son. Odo was in high spirits even though his thrust at the camp of the Saracens had been beaten off.

"It was as you said," the old man crowed. "All that was required was a single threat to the booty they had piled in their tents, and the entire battle line collapsed as their soldiers fled to protect their spoils."

"It was well done, Excellency," Charles nodded and clapped Hunald on the shoulder. "The Aquitanians may be proud of their work, this day." He nodded again. "However, by tomorrow the enemy will have recovered and be ready to meet us again. It would be well for the men to try to get some rest."

Orders were issued for half the men to lie down where they were, with their weapons close to them, while the other half kept watch. What few morsels of food there were were handed around, but no fires were lighted. However, by morning, practically every man was found asleep at his post. Exhaustion had claimed them all.

Charles rode up and down the line and vented his scorn on them in angry words; through no fault of their own they had come safely through the night. It could have been worse, much worse. Saracens could have come up in the darkness and massacred them all! The men accepted this as their due. Even though they had fought hard the day before, there was no reason to get careless.

As the sun rose, the men became restive. Most of the slain lay where they had fallen, but something new hung over the scene. The day before, excitement had filled every heart, but today there was a feeling of emptiness. The fields stretched out on all sides before the men of the north, but the scene was flat and lifeless.

The men looked up; large scavenger birds were circling a clump of trees at some distance. More and more birds were arriving; many had already found perches and were surveying the scene. Men experienced in war know that this happens after the great masses of men have left the field.

When another hour had passed, Charles sent

out his mounted men to reconnoiter. Things were much too quiet; all the Frankish commanders were certain that the Saracens were planning some new devious surprise. Before the Frankish horses could get moving, however, Odo and his Aquitanians set out, heading straight for Poitiers. It was difficult to keep the men in order; excitement had returned but it was a different kind, the kind that stems from an impending unknown.

By the time word reached Charles of what had happened, the counts and barons had about reached the end of their control over the men. As Charles gave the order to advance, many were already running ahead of the line, following Odo's route. Impatience set more and more of them running, although Charles had not told them what the scouts had found.

The entire Saracen camp had been abandoned! There was not one cooking fire, not one warrior to be seen, not a horse nor a mule. The only signs of life were a few Arabs in the tents, too badly wounded to be moved. But what gave the whole situation the wonder of a miracle was that all the plunder, all the riches taken from St. Martin's, Bordeaux, Toulouse, and other towns and villages had been left in the tents. As far as anyone could tell in collecting it, it was all there: the plate, the chalices, the candlesticks, gold and silver coin, dishes of gold, silver crucifixes studded with precious stones, altar cloths, the veils and curtains woven with threads of gold and silver. And there

Many were running ahead of the line.

was more, much more: clothing, dishes, spoil torn from the hands of townspeople, merchandise from many a market place.

Loss of life among the Saracens had been high; massed cavalry charges with no plan, no higher strategy than to ride down the Frank through raw power alone had assured this. Every man who survived must have lost a brother, a father, a cousin, or relative. The Arabs are a "family" people; because of their grief it may have been an easy task for the holy men to point out, as the Arab chroniclers were later to do:

"It was manifest that God's chastisement was sure to follow such excesses; and fortune thereupon turned her back upon the Moslems."

And so it was that during the night, while the Franks slept upon their arms, the entire Saracen host stole forth from the scene with heavy hearts.

At the council of war that took place among the Franks and their allies, Charles made his position clear.

"There are not enough Frankish cavalrymen to pursue the enemy, and the men on foot could never keep up." He looked at Odo. "It is a problem now in the hands of the people of Aquitaine. As the Saracens pass, the Aquitanians by the thousands will rise up out of the ground to keep them moving on to Spain. The noble Duke of Aquitaine will press upon the rear of the enemy and call upon his people to aid him, first, in freeing the country from the invaders, and then in rebuilding the cities and churches which have been destroyed."

Odo looked at Charles as if he didn't believe his ears; Hunald looked startled and then relieved. He smiled and it was clear that the men of Aquitaine were also very eager to get started homeward. Odo's one great worry had been that since he had been unable to stop the Saracen invasion alone and unaided, Charles would move into Aquitaine to take over the country in a kind of protective custody. Now that the force of the Moslem invasion had been broken, Odo's great desire was to go back to his own country and restore it without interference from anyone. Charles' words were almost too good to be true. During the hasty victory celebration which followed, toasts were drunk and pledges were made to confirm a new understanding between Frankland and Aquitaine.

"Now I see that the Frank is the natural brother of the man of Aquitaine." Odo could not take his leave without making at least one speech. "My eyes were blinded to this in the past, as I also failed to see that the Saracen is the natural enemy of both nations. I have a ruined land to remind me of this; moreover, I still have within me the wound in my heart caused by the loss of a daughter, beautiful, beloved of her father."

The old man stared broodingly into his cup. Then he lifted his head and said simply,

"In future, should differences arise between us, let us reason together like men."

Charles nodded and gave Odo his hand, rising to do so. Then he also extended his hand to Hunald.

In the morning, Odo and the Aquitanians departed to the south, while Charles with his troops moved northward to Tours, there to replace the treasure of St. Martin's and accept the plaudits of the townspeople for the victory over the Saracens. Again there was feasting and speechmaking but Charles quickly withdrew his troops across the Loire.

As news from Odo told of a complete withdrawal of the Saracens, Charles returned presently to Paris and then to Metz, being feted and honored for his victory in every town. From this battle, he was named "Martel" ("the Hammer"). Since the ax had always been a favorite weapon of the Franks, perhaps this was thought to be a good symbol for a leader of the Franks. Perhaps the Germanic background of the Frankish people had given this name to Charles in the same sense as Thor, Germanic god of thunder, who was always armed with a hammer. Pictures in ages to come would show Charles leading his troops at the Battle of Tours armed with a huge battle ax.

In Metz, Charles learned that Boniface had been made Archbishop of All the Germans. The title had been conferred by Gregory III, since the previous incumbent of the Holy See had died in

It was all there, the plate, the chalices. . . .

731. Sees had been founded at Erfurt, Eichstadt, Wurzburg, Strassburg, Constanz, Augsburg, Regensburg, Freisingen, Passau, and Fulda. This achievement would not have been possible without the protection of Charles and his Frankish army. Of this Boniface informed the Pope.

There was no rest, however, for the hero of Tours. A rebellion broke out the following year in Frisia, and Charles put it down at the death of the Frisian leader. This time Frisia accepted Christianity. At least, for a time. . . .

Odo, for his part, pursued the Saracens clear to Narbonne as his subjects rallied to his standards, and once again Aquitaine was free of invaders. Again and again Odo attempted to capture Narbonne, the last base of the Saracens in Gaul, but was finally forced to abandon the task.

In spite of this, however, Odo's reputation as a fighting man had grown enormously among the Saracens since Tours, not only because he had threatened their camp at Poitiers and caused their battle line to collapse, but also because of his pursuit of the fleeing enemy through Aquitaine, and his persistent assault on Narbonne.

Never again would Odo rebel against the nominal suzerainty of Charles. Never again would Aquitaine make a separate peace with the Saracens. Odo made it clear to the Arabs that as long as he lived, he was their enemy.

And as long as he lived, the Saracen never invaded his domain again!

CHAPTER NINE

The Saracens' Last Thrust

A funeral procession wound its way through the narrow streets of Toulouse. It was in the Roman style, the funeral litter being borne by eight men preceded by trumpeters, according to custom, since the deceased had not been young. Odo had always thought of himself as a ruler in the Roman tradition; he had dressed as a Roman, according to his times, and now he was being carried to his tomb in the classical manner.

Chief among the mourners, of course, were Hunald and his family, and behind them walked the officials and prefects of Aquitaine. The townspeople looked on in sorrow; to them, their duke had been a great warrior and hero, whatever his mistakes. Ten years before, when Toulouse had been besieged by the Saracens, their duke had returned and driven off the enemy. He had rescued them again after Tours. Most of them had already forgotten the wedding of Lampagie which had played its part in bringing on Rahman's invasion in the first place! And so the people of Toulouse wept as their duke was carried past.

In the ducal palace, Hunald pondered many, many questions. What would happen now? Less than a hundred miles away stood Narbonne, chief city of Septimania and last base of the Saracen in Gaul. His father, the duke, had tried and tried again to capture the city and remove the menace that not only threatened Aquitaine but Burgundy as well.

In council, Hunald put his problems before his advisors: "You have urged me to succeed my father as the Duke of Aquitaine. Some of you have gone farther; you have said that Aquitaine should be proclaimed a kingdom and that I should wear the crown."

The councilors leaned forward, the better to hear. "When one considers the names of the great soldiers of our times, the name of Odo of Aquitaine or Charles the Hammer is mentioned, never that of Hunald."

"That may be now, Excellency," smiled the chamberlain benignly, "but none of us have forgotten that during Rahman's drive to Bordeaux and beyond, you were at your father's side. At Tours you rode beside your father when the Saracens' camp was threatened, you stood with the Franks when the Saracens were turned back—"

"Let the lord Hunald speak!" snapped one of

the elder members of the group. "All these things we know."

Hunald continued. "Now that the renown of my father, the duke, must pass with him into the grave, I must state here and now that I am in favor of stronger ties with the Franks. We need the name of Charles the Hammer as a deterrent to the threat of Saracen aggression. If the Saracens thoroughly understand that any invasion of Aquitaine will bring down upon their heads the full fury of the Franks, I believe that such an invasion will never take place."

The chamber burst into a buzzing of consternation and concern. "But, sir," protested one, "the alliance between Frankland and Aquitaine was informally re-affirmed at Tours!"

Another of the council broke in:

"Your father, the duke, lived all his life in the belief that one day the Franks would add our country to theirs. Now that Charles has withdrawn his troops from our soil after Tours, would you again endanger sovereignty by asking him to be our protector against the Saracens?"

The argument waxed hotter and hotter; many of these men had been the friends of Duke Odo and he had made sure that they all saw things as he did. The meeting broke up without any decision being made.

At the end, Hunald stood up and gave them what he hoped was his last word:

"I had thought, grandes, that I might save our

country from further attack by the Saracens by means of a simple announcement of a strong new treaty with the Franks." He was silent a moment and then burst out, "The Saracens will not rest, I tell you, until they have tested the new ruler of Aquitaine in war!"

One by one, the men of the council visited Hunald privately. All showed grave concern over any move that might indicate to Charles the Hammer that Aquitaine was incapable of handling her own affairs.

"Sir, I am an old man," said one, catching Hunald by the sleeve, "and I had known your father for all our lives. I tell you that Charles is looking for a pretext to invade Aquitaine, to take over the land and add our domain to his own—and always has been."

"Then why didn't he do so after Tours?" Hunald countered hotly. "There we were, our men all crowded together with theirs. Sir, my father and I fully expected it to happen when he got up to speak in council. Instead, he withdrew across the Loire. Why did he not simply march with us to Narbonne? We could have done nothing to prevent it!"

The old councilor wiped his moist brow. What short memories these young people had! He drew a long breath and began again.

"Have you forgotten how Charles invaded Berri and laid siege to Bourges in the spring of the same year that the Saracen attacked?"

For once Hunald had nothing to say.

"When Rahman saw that Charles had invaded Aquitaine from the north, he moved into Gascony," shrilled the old man, waving a finger under Hunald's nose. "Don't tell me it didn't happen, young man! Because it did! I tell you that Charles wanted Rahman to attack Aquitaine—and your father knew it also!"

The sheer enormity of the accusation against Charles stunned the younger man for the moment. He stared long and hard at the aged councilor. "I don't believe it," he said.

"How long, think you, did Charles wait for Neustria to fall into his lap?" Now the old man's voice was low and carried a quaver. "Exactly eleven years. Eleven years, mind you! And he took all of Neustria without raising a lance or drawing a sword."

In the meetings that followed, Hunald found his councilors opposed to his policies almost to a man. Finally, he arose and said:

"Grandes, I know this man. I was present when he took my father under his protection, when we had no place to lay our heads. He fed us and gave us shelter and helped us gather our forces and train new levies. Together we marched to Tours and faced the Saracens. Shoulder to shoulder we stood and beat them back. Then he left us to the remainder of our task and removed his troops from our soil." Hunald's voice shook the roof.

"Grandes, I see no invader in this man!"

Hunald had spoken; each member of the council had spoken. The impasse held. The old saying, "Have a Frank for a friend, but not for a neighbor," seemed to mean—"nor a protector." So thoroughly had Odo drilled his grandes in the single thought.

If Hunald had been partly right in his estimate of the situation, so the council had been partly right. Hunald had said:

"The Saracens will not rest until they have tested the new ruler of Aquitaine in war."

The councilors had insisted that Charles Martel had been looking for any pretext to take over Aquitaine and add it to his own lands.

It was still the year of Odo's death, 735, and without the renowned Duke Odo to hinder them, the Saracens issued from Narbonne and seized Arles and Avignon! At about the same time, Charles Martel at the head of his battle-tried veterans crossed the Loire and plunged deep into Aquitaine! Before Hunald and his brother Hatto could prevent it, the Frank had seized Bordeaux and Blaye.

The two brothers met Charles at Bordeaux. Charles, after taking sudden action and giving no warning, was waiting in his customary way to see what would result. He had destroyed nothing; as in the campaign against Bourges in 732, he had moved quickly and seized an important city. The next move was up to Hunald.

An enraged Hunald was ushered into the presence of the Frankish leader. He had been the man who had stood up to his councilors as being in favor of a stronger alliance with Charles Martel. He had been the *only* one who had favored such a thing. And now the old men had been shown to be right. Perhaps, though, something could be saved from the situation.

"The last time I had the honor of speaking with you, my lord, was near Poitiers, the scene of a great battle." Charles acted as if his whole action was nothing more nor less than an informal social call. "Since then I have learned with sorrow of the death of your father, the duke."

Hunald and Hatto bowed without speaking. Hunald could not have spoken if his life depended on it.

"In the past, I refrained from entering into the conflict with the Saracen until your father, the duke, sought my help. This was the costly way, I own; the city in which we stand at this moment has barely been healed of her scars." However Charles Martel spoke, his words were falling on deaf ears. Hunald was aware of the sounds of the older man's voice as he went on and on trying to soothe, to heal, to show the reasonableness of his present action.

Hunald owned himself to have been a fool. Oh, the old men had been right; his father, the duke, had been right! Self-interest was the only motivation that this man knew; any thoughts to the contrary were ruinous. He blurted out, at last:

"My brother and I are here to learn of your terms. May we have them now?"

Charles' eyebrows shot up. "I don't understand. What terms are you talking about?"

"Sir, we are not children! You have invaded our country without warning or cause. I can only surmise that you are planning to annex Aquitaine as you have taken Neustria and annexed the lands of the Germans." His body shook with suppressed rage. "And to think that I, alone, of all the council stood for a stronger alliance with the Franks. No, they said, for Charles seeks to annex our land; to seek an alliance with the Frankish lion is to be eaten whole."

Hatto spoke, almost wonderingly:

"This is true, sir."

Charles nodded understandingly. His whole mien was that of a kindly old uncle who had looked in on his nephews to see if they lacked for anything. At no time in his life had Hunald felt more like a child; this man of the north, with his world of experience, had won fully as many battles through guile as he had through the power of the sword.

The wound in the heart and soul of the younger man was deep and festering; it was destined never to heal. It would finally bring him to his end in obscurity and exile.

Quickly now, Charles sketched out his plan. If Hunald would swear an oath of fealty to him now—and Hatto—that would be all that he

would require. He was on his way to Lyon, the
capital of Burgundy. Using Lyon as a base, he
would drive south and push the Saracen back to
Narbonne and beyond. This would benefit Aquitaine as well as Burgundy and go a long way toward preventing another wholesale invasion of
Gaul.

"And if I refuse to take such an oath?" Hunald
could not forbear saying.

"But you will."

"And if I don't?" Hunald persisted.

"Why, then, I would hold the country for as
long as I thought best and rule through another
duke, whom I should select." Charles' voice was
very gentle.

The brothers took the oath.

Perched on a hill above the confluence of the
Rhone and Saône rivers stood the city of Lyon, or
Lugdunum, as the Romans had called it. Five
great roads radiated from it. Two led into Aquitaine and to the Atlantic Ocean, one led to the
Rhinelands, another to Italy, and the remaining
one to the Mediterranean. Three towns, hardly
more than villages at the time, surrounded it: Roman Fourviere, the Gallic Condate on the slopes
of present-day Croix Russe, and the settlement of
boatmen and merchants on the Isle of Ainay. The
district was rapidly filling up with Frankish soldiers ready and eager to meet the Saracens again.
The Burgundians, for their part, watched all this

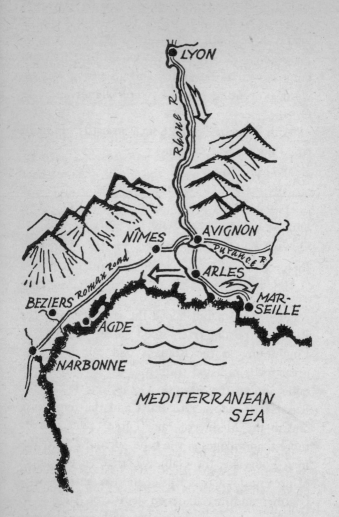

LYON

Rhone R.

AVIGNON

Durance R.

NÎMES

Roman Road

ARLES

MAR-
SEILLE

BEZIERS

AGDE

NARBONNE

MEDITERRANEAN
SEA

with mingled feelings. Some pointed out that Charles had passed this way sixteen years before. He had secured their allegiance and then departed. This time he had come by way of Aquitaine. As far as anyone knew, he had left Aquitaine intact. Others, however, feared the Franks as much as the Saracens.

Charles called a council of the nobles and clergy of Burgundy. Once the Saracens had been removed from the scene, he pointed out, there would be a need for judges and officials to see that in running the affairs of Burgundy the province might remain strong. Some of the appointments were made on the spot, and other men would be appointed in the various towns and villages.

And so the armies got under way, moving down the Rhone Valley to Avignon.

Whenever Saracen bands were seen during the march of nearly one hundred and fifty miles, they seemed to draw back as if they had been actually waiting for some enemy to appear and drive them off. The vigor of Abd-ar-Rahman was missing.

The Franks halted in sight of the town while the horsemen scouted the vicinity.

The city stood on the east bank of the Rhone. In the river lay the island that has since come to be known as Ile de la Barthelasse, but due to the swiftness of the current there was no bridge leading to the west bank of the small settlement there. All was quiet—ominously so—as the Franks took in the situation. The order was given to march again and the troops sealed off the town.

In doing this, however, some of the mounted men came upon a small force of Saracens at the juncture of the Rhone and Durance rivers. It was a key point; there were roads leading to Avignon from the east which followed the Durance Valley. In the action that followed, a number of prisoners were taken who confirmed what the Franks were becoming aware of—that the city of Avignon had been abandoned.

Immediately Charles' troops marched in and took the city while others were ordered on to Arles. For the moment, Charles established his headquarters here and set up courts and appointed judges for the area. The citizens, most of whom had fled the town, were now drifting back and the rejoicing became general.

As the Franks pushed on and invested Arles, another wing of the army pressed on to Marseille. Again, the mere show of force seemed to be sufficient; the Saracens withdrew almost as if by agreement.

The only real encounter with the Saracen was on the Berre River near Narbonne itself. Here Charles drove the Saracens back into their stronghold. But in the midst of his preparations to besiege the town, word came that a number of German tribes had risen in revolt, that his attention was needed in the north. Charles hurried off at the head of his Franks, and the Burgundians settled down to a very dubious peace.

Two years later, the Saracen again issued from his base and seized Arles and Avignon.

This time Charles met with a new ally, probably somewhere on the Durance River. This was young Liutprand, King of the Lombards and Charles' brother-in-law. He was about twenty-five at the time and in some ways like Charles. Most of his career seemed to be before him and he was eager to win a name for himself.

Charles explained what he had in mind with regard to the Saracens.

"Many attempts have been made to drive the enemy out of Gaul but as each attempt has failed, the Saracen, at his own good time, continually issues from his stronghold and attacks Burgundy or Aquitaine." Charles sighed. "Once it took all the resources of Aquitaine and Frankland to drive him back at Tours. This must never happen again."

The young man nodded. Naturally ambitious, it would not hurt his career in the least to have a campaign or two with this famous soldier and increase his own reputation. If his reputation were to become great and powerful enough, he would need only to appear on the field and an enemy of lesser assurance or renown would often withdraw. It was as simple as that.

"Say on, brother. You will find me eager to listen."

Charles' eyes twinkled for the moment; in the matter of titles he was "Mayor of the Palace," which was the name, actually, of an official only. Liutprand, for his part, was a full-fledged king, sovereign of Lombardy, with the dukes of Spoleto and Beneventum as his vassals. Charles may have reflected that since Thierry, royal successor to Chilpèric, had recently passed away, it would be a simple matter to have himself elevated to the royal line if only he were to give the word. However, at the moment, this may not have seemed important!

"In my position, it is impossible to be everywhere at once," he continued, "even though it has been necessary in the past. Each time I am occupied elsewhere, the Saxons, or the Alemanni, or the Bavarians, or any number of other tribes rise up in my rear and set my labors at naught. When we have finished our campaigns here, however, I hope to have made it clear to the Saracens that any new disturbances on their part will bring you on the scene, a matter of serious consideration."

Both laughed; this would suit the young king perfectly. "Then," vowed Charles, "let the Germans beware!"

Both were pleased with the arrangement, and the pact was made, signed, and sealed. For Charles it meant that a watchdog would be set on this corner of the Moslem world, an actual member of the family, at least by marriage! As for Liutprand, it would hurt no ruler to have been an ally of Charles Martel for a campaign or two.

The Franks and the Lombard allies got under way and marched on Avignon and Arles. Both towns fell to them, but a part of the Saracen forces withdrew to Nîmes. Charles and the King of the Lombards bypassed the city and pushed on to Agde and Beziers.

The two leaders worked well together; Charles was pleased to have an ally who waited for him to make the plans and give the orders without rushing off in all directions to do something brilliant on his own.

"And now," said Charles one day, "we will be coming in sight of Agde. Perhaps they will open their gates to us. The city will be easy to defend for a time but it is almost impossible to retreat from it."

"My guess is they will not defend it," Liutprand opined. "They've probably left the city by ship."

They came upon Agde at the foot of an extinct volcano two and a half miles from the mouth of the Herault River. The houses were built, for the most part, of the dark volcanic basalt emitted by the old crater in times past. Liutprand was wrong, however. The walls were fully defended.

The allies decided in any case to bypass this town also and turn their attention to Beziers.

They marched to Beziers and attacked the hill on which it stands on the east bank of the Orb. The Roman road crosses the river at this point on its way to Narbonne and Spain. Many Saracens were leaving the city even now. Perhaps having a river at their back made them nervous.

Charles was in sight of Narbonne, having taken Beziers according to plan, and was marshaling all his forces for the assault. If he could capture this last base of the Saracen in Gaul, he would have succeeded where Odo had tried many times in vain. There was no reason why the allies should not conquer this time. In any case, the peace of Gaul depended on it.

Narbonne, a heavily walled city, stood on the shores of a lake fed in those times by the River Aude. Here the Romans had built great stoneworks to protect this inland harbor, and a Roman fleet had been based here to protect the western end of the Mediterranean. Later it had taken two years for the Saracens to capture the city, but once having secured it, no one had been able to drive them out! This was a challenge worthy of any warrior's mettle. The Franks and their Lombard allies lunged to the attack.

Hardly had the assault begun when word reached Charles that the Saracens based at Nîmes were pouring out of the city and attacking the force he had set to watch it. This, of course, threatened his own line of communications, and reluctantly he withdrew from the walls of Narbonne. He was still mindful of Agde, too.

Perhaps as the outstanding soldier of his time, Charles had begun to underestimate his opponent. Strategy had never been a strong point with the Saracen; at least examples of it were rare, so far. That the Moslems should see an opportunity to flank Charles Martel and his allies probably didn't seem too likely, but Charles doubtless was forced to admit to himself that to strike at Narbonne, without dealing with Nîmes and Agde first, was hardly the decision of a prudent man!

Charles now shifted the bulk of his troops northward, assaulted Agde, and set Beziers on fire to keep the city out of enemy hands.

"The Saracens are being driven back on Nîmes," reported the commander of the division which had been assigned the task of containing this portion of the enemy, "although it is still early to tell the outcome."

Charles, together with Liutprand, surveyed the situation. The city itself lay at the foot of the Garrigues range of barren hills which closed off this shelf of land from the rest of Gaul. To the north of the town was a tall hill crested with a tower built by the Romans. Charles surveyed this with interest.

"I see an aqueduct leading from the hills to the hill on which the tower stands. By cutting off the water supply we can shorten the time of siege."

"We had already thought of this, Excellency," the paladin said, "but there is a reservoir below the tower which can supply the enemy for months. To destroy the aqueduct would make little difference."

"Then we shall proceed with a direct assault,"

Charles decided. The armies of the Franks and their allies were concentrated in the plains of the Vistre now, and the Saracens had withdrawn almost to a man into the shelter of the city.

Augustus had fortified Nîmes with ninety towers and ten gates, when he had settled a colony of veteran legionnaires here in Roman times. The four miles of defensive walls were a military man's dream. Charles and his allies knew that, while these fortifications were no longer in first class condition, it would be a task of the first magnitude to drive out the enemy.

Nîmes had been a luxury city once, and abounded with baths and fountains that graced many lovely gardens among temples and basilicas.

There had been theaters also and an amphitheater built to seat twenty-four thousand people. This circus structure, as it happened, was to serve the Saracens in an unexpected way; unexpected insofar as Charles and the allies were concerned.

The Franks assaulted the city with all their resources, and after days of hard fighting, some of the walls were breached and the men-at-arms poured through. Fighting in the streets followed, hand to hand, up one street and down another. Fires broke out and the smoke brought confusion to the knots of men struggling all over the city in the cramped areas.

However, the bulk of the Saracen forces had shut themselves up in the old Roman amphithe-

The Franks assaulted the city.

ater and were using it as a fort. The four gates were closed and barricaded, and the structure was so well built that Charles could make no impression on it. In centuries to come, as a matter of fact, this old amphitheater, gift of Nero to the city, would serve other warriors in just such a way.

Charles, in his direct way, attempted to set it on fire. Wave after wave of men piled thousands of bundles of faggots against the stonework as the Saracens hurled clouds of javelins down upon the Franks. As the flames mounted, vast clouds of smoke arose and perhaps the smoke was more to be feared than the fire itself. A stiff breeze fanned the fumes into the amphitheater, and in a short time the Saracens began to surrender in batches; those who could fled back to Narbonne. The city was combed for groups of Moslems who had concealed themselves among ruins of many a handsome building. In this way the city fell. More than twelve hundred years later the smoke marks on the walls of the amphitheater would be pointed out as the work of Charles Martel when he stormed and captured Nîmes.

It was perhaps during the time when Charles was setting up prefects and judges in the captured cities, with every inclination toward peace and order, that war came again. This time a Moorish leader by the name of Maurontus rose up in rebellion in Provence, and Charles, with his ally Liutprand, hurried off to put it down.

CHAPTER TEN
A Plea for Help

Charles Martel and Liutprand, King of the Lombards, marched against Maurontus, the Moor. Among the banners of the paladins of Charles' army now fluttered the standards of his brother Childebrand. The reconciliation may have taken place about the time of the assault on Avignon or Arles. At any rate, both brothers rejoiced in the reunion and the past was officially forgotten. From the line of Childebrand would come the Capets, house of Robert the Strong.

Childebrand had brought news from home. Rotruda was still with the two boys in Lombardy, where she had fled to her family when Charles had brought home Swanhilda, the Bavarian, from his campaign on the Danube in 728. The officials left in charge at home seemed to be fulfilling their duties under the eyes of the Church and all seemed quiet. As usual, however, the Germans

were threatening another uprising, and Swanhilda, Charles' new companion, was protesting
the continued absence of her Frankish lord.

"Help me with this campaign, my brother,"
Charles entreated, "and we will return to Germany together. This time we will annex all of the
south German lands as I once did in Frisia."

Childebrand listened to his brother as he talked
on different matters but said nothing. It seemed
to him that Charles was different, somehow.
There was no sign yet of any weakening of his
ability to deliver quick thrusts and lightning-like
blows whenever needed, but Childebrand noticed
that Charles often seemed weary. This had never
been the case before; Charles Martel had become
a legendary figure because, for one thing, he had
always had an abundance of energy. Long swift
marches along the hard surfaces of the Roman
roads, rain, hail, winds, heat, cold, all were the
natural elements in which this warrior thrived.

Still, with Liutprand and his Lombards, the
two brothers rode against the Moor and beat him
into submission. When Provence was again quiet
and there was no sound from Narbonne, the rumors of German activity in the North became
louder. Perhaps it were better to return to Narbonne and complete the work of driving out the
Saracen from Gaul. Instead, Charles made his ar-
rangements with Liutprand.

In their leave-taking, wherein many toasts were
drunk, many pledges made, and protestations of

loyalty heard on every side, Charles said at one
point:

"It will be necessary for the Saracen to learn
and remember that, despite my absence from Provence or Septimania, the men of Lombardy are
close at hand."

Liutprand beamed at the words; he felt that
with these words he had been acknowledged by
his honored preceptor to be a man to be reckoned
with as a soldier. Charles went on to recommend
that the Lombards keep the Saracen under surveillance at all times. Not only were they to be vigi-
lant, but at the first sign of any activity in the re-
gion of Narbonne, they were to move in quickly
before trouble got started.

"Strike down the standards of the Saracen
whenever the opportunity presents itself," he
urged. "Show them no rest until that day when
Gaul shall be free of them." He sighed and then
quickly threw off the great wave of weariness
which had suddenly threatened to engulf him.

Liutprand graciously thanked Charles for his
expression of confidence and also for what he had
been privileged to learn of the arts of war under
Charles' tutelage. Formally, he offered to convey
Charles' greetings to Rotruda and the boys when
he returned home.

Perhaps Charles had hoped that this assign-
ment of watching over this portion of Gaul
would give the eager young king something to oc-
cupy his talents. If so, Hunald would also benefit,

and Charles could be free to attend to other problems.

And so the allies parted—the Franks to go north to deal with the Germans and the Lombards to go eastward to Italy.

The year 738 found Charles again fighting in Germany in an effort to bring permanent order to that tempestuous land. This time he went ahead with his plans to consolidate the south German lands into the Frankish domain. The campaigns, however, now seemed Herculean; the more one wielded the sword, the more there was to be done. To put down an insurrection in one locality was to know that future tempests were already brewing. To Charles, as the years passed, it seemed that the fighting would never end; what had begun as a challenge had become an endless treadmill.

A man of war in those times needed youth, energy, and good fortune. When youth passed and energy began to flag, the end was in sight. Charles was fifty now, an elderly man by the standards of the times, but there was something else. The illness that was finally to stop his warrior's heart was beginning to make its appearance.

This was the situation when the papal envoys from Rome reached Charles in Germany. The tidings, as might be expected, had to do with violent happenings in far-off places that needed Charles' attention at once.

The envoys were two, a Bishop Anastasius and

Sergius, a priest. While the first message from Gregory III has been lost to us, certainly the envoys supplied Charles with the background of the new developments.

Charles was reclining in his litter under the trees in the grip of his great weariness as Anastasius told the story.

"Flushed with the success of his campaign in Provence, Liutprand, King of the Lombards, resolved to end the power of the eastern Roman Empire in Italy," Anastasius declared angrily. "However, when the dukes of Spoleto and Beneventum opposed him, Liutprand attacked them both and drove their armies back upon Rome, where they took refuge."

Charles listened carefully. Here was a very embarrassing dilemma indeed. Once the Saracen learned of Liutprand's involvement at Rome, there would certainly be some sort of activity in the vicinity of Narbonne. There was bound to be.

"I am listening," Charles said. Perhaps he had not told them that his eldest son, Carloman, recently returned from Lombardy, had given Liutprand's account of his dissatisfaction with the authority of Constantinople. This was the first time Charles had learned that Liutprand had taken steps in the matter. Though irritated beyond measure by the young king's precipitate action, Charles gave no sign of that irritation to the papal legation.

"We bear the chains of St. Peter and the keys to

the Holy Sepulchre," the bishop continued, "and the Holy Father would place in your hands the protectorate of Rome if your Excellency will only come quickly and help us."

The urgency of the message was not lost on the ruler of the Franks but there were certain difficulties and obstacles.

The legation continued to bring pressure; confidentially, they implied that the nobility of Rome earnestly desired Frankish protection also. They would even renounce the Emperor at Constantinople!

Ever since Constantinople had become the capital of the Roman Empire, the Romans of Italy had grown increasingly powerless. Constantinople was too far away, and the Church had to step in as the Emperor's representative in Italy. The Lombards, however, wanted to do away with the rule of the Emperor at Constantinople completely. Many Romans felt the same way.

Obviously torn between the Pope's appeal and the loyalty he felt toward a former ally, Charles dissolved the meeting and retired to rest. He heaped presents upon the envoys later and promised to send his own envoys to visit the Holy See.

The scribes worked long and hard on Charles' message to Gregory, and envoys were chosen to travel with it to Rome. There were many presents also. Grimo, Abbot of Corbie, and Sigebert, a monk of St. Denis, would form Charles' legation to the Pope.

Gregory had finished repairing the walls of Rome at his own expense. This had included the fortifications of the old city, called Centumcellae. It was fortunate that he did so; the fortifications were now being put to the test. Liutprand was continuing his attempts to hasten the crumbling of the Roman Empire.

A second letter reached Charles.

"Our affliction moves us to write you again, trusting that you are a loving son of St. Peter, and of us, and that, from respect for him, you will come and defend the Church of God . . . now unable to endure the persecution and oppression of the Lombards. They have seized the very means set aside to furnish funds for the lights kept ever burning at St. Peter's tomb, and they have carried off offerings that have been made by you and by those who have gone before you. And because, after God, we have turned to you, the Lombards deride and oppress us. Hence, the Church of St. Peter has been stripped and reduced to the last straits. We have put into the mouth of the bearer of this letter, your faithful servant, all our woes, which he will be able to unfold to you."

This missive was concluded with the repeated plea that Charles would come at once.

By a strange coincidence the arrival of Grimo and Sigebert in Rome happened to occur at the same time that Liutprand withdrew his troops to Pavia! Charles, the man of imagination and action, seemed somehow to forget the "power of the written word," the happy phrase of Boniface, that is, poised force not used. Perhaps if Charles had written a letter directly to Liutprand, underlining certain key words, Liutprand might have postponed his plans or even given them up. The Lombard might well have hesitated to risk combat with his old instructor! At any rate, Charles evidently did not think of communicating with Liutprand at this time.

Such was not the case with the King of the Lombards, however. His embassy reached Charles shortly afterward.

The German campaign had lost something of its vigor due to the ailments of the Frankish commander, but the Lombards reached him just as the papal envoys had. Charles' illness was more obvious now; he received them as a sick man who ruled only a sick room. The Lombards noticed this part of the situation with real interest.

"And what has that rascally brother-in-law of mine done now?" It was not exactly an invalid's whine but there was irritation in the tone. The man of battle now seemed to yearn for peace, to be left alone entirely.

"The King of the Lombards sends his greetings to a noble soldier and a well-loved brother-in-law," began the envoy in a high voice, "and begs to inform him that all is well with his beloved wife and young Pepin, his son. The climate of Lombardy appears to agree with them both."

"Well, well," grunted Charles, as the envoy

looked up from his scroll. "I am sure there is little harm in either of them. But what of Liutprand, King of the Lombards? It strikes me that the world has been hearing quite a little of him lately."

The ambassadors bowed and smiled. Yes, the young king seemed well on the road to making a name for himself. Perhaps it might not be too much to say—

"Yes, yes," growled Charles. "No doubt some day he will be master of all Italy. What else does he say?"

With many gestures of eloquent self-deprecation, the man went on to suggest that numerous questions might have risen in the mind of the Frankland's mayor of the palace as to the situation in Lombardy and Rome. His Excellency should know—indeed, was entitled to know—that Liutprand had no wish to wage war in Italy, that the whole affair had started when he had been forced to punish two rebellious vassals. These, of course, were the dukes of Spoleto and Beneventum, who had insisted upon upholding the authority of the Emperor in Constantinople. Everyone knew, of course, that Italy and its affairs should be—must be—in the hands of those who actually lived in Italy. There was a lot more along these lines, but suddenly Charles became aware that the author of the letter was making some very pointed references to the fact that Pepin, his young son, was after all in his custody—or perhaps *protection* would be a better word. Also, much was made of family ties, by marriage as well as by blood, and, of course, the memory of glorious days spent in slaughtering the Saracens.

As in so many instances these days, Charles put off giving an answer. The envoys, despairing of any quick action, asked for and got permission to return to Italy.

They arrived in the court of Liutprand with word that Charles Martel no longer constituted a threat to the ambitions of Lombardy. The mayor of the palace was ill, they said—and would be in no position to intervene in their affairs or to give aid to the Pope. This had been an estimate of the situation developed on the way back to Italy by the two envoys, and Liutprand listened eagerly.

The day when the threat of Charles' action could pacify an unruly neighbor had passed, as of this moment. In 740 Liutprand took to the field and the war was on again.

A third message from Gregory reached Charles.

"We were overwhelmed with grief when we saw the little that was left from last year for the support of the poor of Christ and the upkeep of the church lamps in the Ravenese district, laid waste with fire and sword by the King of the Lombards. Moreover, to these parts also have they dispatched troops. They have destroyed the farms of St. Peter, and the cattle which still remained to us they have carried off. Not only have we not received any help from you, but as you have not checked the warlike action of the king, it is clear that you have paid more attention to their version of the affair than you have to ours, true though it be. The result is that you, yourself, are even derided by them: 'Let Charles and his Franks come and save you from us if they can.' By the power given him by God, St. Peter could defend his own; but he would try his faithful children."

Gregory's account of the damage caused by the ambitious Liutprand now turned to a plea for understanding of the accused vassals.

"You must not believe what the Lombard king urges against the dukes of Spoleto and Beneventum. . . . Their only offense is that last year they refused to make an inroad upon us." Later the Holy Father urged:

"Still, that you may know the truth for yourself, send a faithful agent who cannot be bribed and let him see what we have to suffer, and then report everything to you."

Then came the last agonized plea:

"I adjure thee, in the Name of the True and Living God and by the keys of St. Peter's Confession which I sent thee, not to prefer the friendship of a king of the Lombards to that of the Prince of the Apostles, but to come quickly to our aid."

There was more to the story. Transemund, Duke of Spoleto, had taken advantage of Liutprand's withdrawal of 739 and collected a large army of Romans. Entering the duchy from two directions, Transemund regained his domain. He seemed to have a very short memory indeed. Once having recovered his own, he seemed content to forget his benefactors. Gregory had counted on his help in restoring four border towns to the Roman duchy which the Lombards had captured earlier in the war. When the Duke of Spoleto continued to ignore Gregory's urgings, Gregory determined to get Liutprand himself to restore the cities.

Anastasius and the regionary subdeacon, Adeodatus, formed the legation this time. They carried a letter to the bishops of Lombardy and Tuscany, reminding them of their oaths to help the Holy See whenever it was in trouble or danger.

But the Pope himself was ill, by this time. His letter read in part:

"Weak as I am from illness, if, as I will not believe, you should refrain from giving your help and going with my ambassadors, I will undertake the journey myself and save you from the responsibility of being unfaithful to your obligations."

Liutprand, however, would not listen. It remained for Gregory's successor, Zachary, to make a personal appeal to the Lombard king and through the great personal magnetism of the man, to persuade Liutprand to give back the four cities: Amelia, Orte, Bomarzo, and Bidea. By the time this happened, however, Charles Martel and the Emperor Leo of Constantinople would be in their graves for a year or more.

While the dying Charles Martel was still lying at Quiersey-sur-Oise, he sent for his sons, Carloman and Pepin. Like one of the old kings of the royal line of Meroveus, he divided up Frankland between them quite as if he had the right. After all, as mayor of the palace he was merely an official. As he himself had said many years before, he was not even a noble.

Nevertheless, Pepin became mayor of the palace of Neustria, Carloman that of Austrasia, and the old divisions were restored again in the land. Upon his signature, all that Charles had planned for and fought for was reduced to the fragments in which he had found the country when he had come to power. There was some difference of course. Carloman's portion included not only Austrasia but also Alemannia and Thuringia, with suzerainty over Bavaria. Pepin's domain, too, was larger; he ruled over Neustria and Burgundy as well as Provence.

Just before the end, Charles roused from his deep languor long enough to say,

"Where is your mother, boy?"

Carloman and Pepin, both grown men and rulers now in their own right, looked at each other helplessly.

"Well, where is she? You there." He peered at Pepin and shook his head dubiously. "I don't know you, do I?"

Swanhilda, kneeling by the bedside, wept the more as she perceived that the mind of "the Hammer" was going fast. Charles now turned to her, thinking her to be Rotruda, mother of Carloman and Pepin. Softly, his voice quavering from weakness, he said,

"I could wish that we had spent more time together—but no. First there was prison—and then wars to be won—always wars—always and always. And now there is no time. No more time. I am so sorry, my dear."

He lived for several hours after that but he said nothing more. Of course the very presence of Swanhilda was sufficient to keep Rotruda far from the scene, but it may have been that Carloman or perhaps Pepin found a way to tell their mother that Charles' last thoughts had been of her.

Charles, the Hammer, died in October, 741, at Quiersey-sur-Oise and was buried at St. Denis, near Paris.

It was Carloman, of course, who hastened to approach Boniface about a matter that had troubled him for some time. He requested that Boniface conduct a synod in Frankland to restore the discipline in the Church which had been neglected for many years. In writing to Pope Zachary about the matter, Boniface said,

"The Franks, as our elders report, have not held a synod for more than eighty years, nor had an

Charles Martel was lying at Quiersey-sur-Oise.

archbishop, nor founded or renewed the canons of the Church."

As a result of Carloman's desire for apostolic sanction, the synod took place in April of 742 at Mainz. Boniface himself presided over the reorganization of the Frankish Church.

Another matter was dealt with at the Council of Lestines two years after Charles' death. This time both Carloman and Pepin were present at a meeting called to examine what came to be known as the "Secularization of Charles." The matter of the praecariums and the benefices troubled many people, not the least of whom were Charles' two sons. Charles had been accused of perpetrating and condoning certain acts against the best interests of the Church. Later he had seemed to reverse himself and work with the Church.

Pardoned to a certain extent by the Council, since the Church after all did own the property regardless of who had had its administration, an attempt was made to clear Charles' name of certain persistent charges. It was not entirely successful, however. Over a thousand years later, Gibbon would write:

"—after his death his merits were forgotten . . . his sacrilege alone remembered."

Fortunately, however, for the people of Frankland and perhaps for the future country that would be known as France, events took an upward turn. If the sick man at Quiersey had managed to set his life's work at naught in his fevered moments by dividing his domain between his two sons, there were other forces evidently at work. In 747, after six years of ruling Austrasia as its mayor of the palace, Carloman abdicated in favor of his younger brother Pepin. This, of course, allowed for the restoration of the political unity of the Frankish nation.

Carloman retired to Montecassino in Italy, a great monastery of St. Benedict which had been empty for one hundred years. It had been restored by Liutprand shortly before his death in 744. Twelve hundred years later, a retreating German army would use the buildings as a fortress to hold up an allied offensive in World War II.

A second factor in the unification of Frankland would come through a son born to Pepin III, a year after the death of Charles Martel. This was Charles' namesake, later to be known as Charlemagne, Emperor of the Holy Roman Empire. He would build on the structure begun by his grandfather and secure the foundations for the French nation.

Gaul had been conquered by the Franks coming across the Rhine a few thousand at a time. The civilized Gallo-Romans accepted the rule of these warriors since the protectors, the legions of Rome, had been withdrawn. The Germanic tongue, spoken by the Franks, became gradually mixed with the Gallo-Latin of the inhabitants and as time went by, they forgot their Roman culture. Hundreds of years passed; the descendants of the conquered people forgot even how to read and write. They came to depend on the Frankish nobles for protection, like helpless children. Out of this predicament grew the system of feudalism, which later came to be remembered chiefly for its abuses.

To the Germanic tribes born to the idea that war was the normal means for settling differences, Charles Martel entered the scene as the greatest warrior of them all. Yet he spent his whole life and all his talents as a soldier to set up a stabilized nation where, in time, civilization could be reborn.

Civilization, however, is not established by diligently putting down an endless series of rebellions by the force of arms. Christianity was the influence which Boniface, the "Apostle of Germany," attempted to establish everywhere he went. More quickly than anyone had a right to expect, the civilizing influence manifested itself in the lives of the tribes, even though the old habits were still strong.

Boniface knew that he was not preaching to empty minds and hearts among the Germans. On the contrary, the fearful images of the warrior gods, which kept the Germanic mind permanently inflamed, had first to be displaced. This task he carried out until his death at Dokkum at the hands of the Frisians in 754. He was buried at

Fulda where to this day the German bishops still meet.

Later, the goals of both Charles Martel and Boniface would be combined to a degree in the career of Charlemagne. At Tours, where his grandfather had turned back the Saracen, Charlemagne would set up his "Palace School" under the tutelage of Alcuin, the British monk. In this way the lamp of knowledge would be rekindled; its light would grow and spread until Frankland would develop as a great center of culture in its own right.

Before this could happen, however, order had to be brought to Gaul, and this was the personal mission of Charles Martel. He was a man who held to his decisions come what might. However difficult this may have been for his family and friends, it was this quality in him which was most needed at that time in that country which we now call France.

For More about Charles Martel

Creasey, Edward S. *Fifteen Decisive Battles of the World*. Harrisburg, Pennsylvania: The Stackpole Co., 1957.

Fuller, J. F. C. *Military History of the Western World*, Vol. 1. New York: Funk & Wagnalls Co., Inc., 1954.

Lamb, Harold. *Charlemagne: the legend and the man*. New York: Doubleday & Company, Inc., 1954.

Reinhardt, Kurt. *Germany: 2000 Years*. Rev. ed., 2 vols. New York: Frederick Ungar Publishing Co., Inc.

Van Dyke, Paul. *The Story of France*. New York: Charles Scribner's Sons, 1928.

The Author and His Book

Shane Miller was born in Reading, Pennsylvania, and was educated at the Pennsylvania School of Industrial Art in Philadelphia and the Art Students' League and the New School, both in New York City. His first piece of published writing appeared in a newspaper when he was in the sixth grade. After leaving art school, he joined a classmate in establishing an art service agency in Philadelphia. Following the event of the depression, Mr. Miller left the firm and came to New York City where, for several years, he designed displays and wrote stories and articles for magazines. From 1937 to 1948 he created the scenics for full-color animated films released by Paramount Pictures. Mr. Miller's career in children's books began in 1950 when he illustrated *Merry Men of Gotham* by M. Jagendorf (Vanguard Press, 1950). Since then he has illustrated books for many publishers. He has both written and illustrated *Peter Stuyvesant's Drummer* (Coward-McCann, Inc., 1959) and *The Romans,* a volume in the *Life Long Ago* series (Coward-McCann, Inc., 1963). Married, Mr. Miller is a resident of White Plains, New York, and maintains a studio in New York City.

INDEX